PIC Basics

a practical guide to using PICs

Cliff Powlesland, G8CQZ

Radio Society of Great Britain

PIC BASICS

Published by the Radio Society of Great Britain, Cranborne Road, Potters Bar, Herts EN6 3JE.

First published 2006

ISBN 1-905086-18-0
EAN 978-1905-086-18-4

Publisher's note
The opinions expressed in this book are those of the author and not necessarily those of the RSGB. While the information presented is believed to be correct, the author, publisher and their agents cannot accept responsibility for consequences arising from any inaccuracies or omissions.

Typography and design: Mike Dennison, G3XDV, Emdee Publishing
Cover design: Dorotea Vizer
Production: Mark Allgar, M1MPA

Printed in Great Britain by Page Bros of Norwich

The full program listings, as printed in the Appendix to this book, and additional data can be found at
www.rsgb.org/books/extra/picbasics.htm

Contents

Introduction

 icrochip Technology Inc., of Chandler, Arizona in the USA, have designed a number of different types of Integrated Circuit chips which they market under the generic name of 'PIC'. Although each chip type has different capabilities, they can include:

- Numerous input/output signals that operate at logic levels
- Timers and counters
- Analogue to digital converters
- Circuits to communicate with PCs and other PIC chips.

All PIC chips require programming before they can be used.

I use a lot of PIC chips in my projects. I find them cheap, simple to use and easy to obtain. However, I know that a number of my fellow Radio Amateurs do not like PICs.

Many less experienced constructors have tried building projects that include PIC chips. Sometimes, the chip has failed to program and they have not had enough experience to know why this has happened. Others, who have sent away for pre-programmed chips or who have spent hours typing in code that they did not understand, say that they have found the process deeply dissatisfying. Often, these projects are designed to show how much can be done by just one chip and so the programs are complex and use 'clever' routines that make understanding difficult. In addition, these projects often have many complex features that are of little use to real Radio Amateurs. Some Radio Amateurs have tried to learn about the PIC but have found that most books and articles are aimed at computer experts. However, experienced computer programmers often find the restrictions of the PIC, compared to computers such as the PC, to be onerous.

I don't. I find the restrictions to be the strength of the PIC and that is one of the reasons that I have written this book. It is probably best if you do not have a computer programming background or you treat PIC programming as being an entirely different discipline.

The projects that I provide are not new but (hopefully) they are both useful and relatively simple. Most are built on stripboard and each project has a full description of how the software works. My aim is to show you how the PIC works in 'real world' projects so that you can see how useful PICs can be in your own projects - and how to tackle the task.

Cliff Powlesland, G8CQZ

What is a PIC?

T o say that a PIC chip is a microprocessor is unfair, although the description is accurate. PIC chips can only multiply or divide by two, can rarely work with numbers above 255 and most have less than 100 bytes of random access memory (RAM). But they do have advantages over other chips. These advantages include:

- The fact that each chip contains the processor, program memory, data memory, interrupt handler and input/output functions that it requires
- A fixed instruction execution time that makes it easier to create programs for time critical applications
- Chips that contain built in functions such as counters, analogue to digital converters and communications
- A simple instruction set that is easy to learn.

Choosing a PIC

Never choose a PIC, for a new project, on the basis of a catalogue description as these are often misleading. For example, a 16F73 chip may have 22 digital input/output (I/O) pins, 5 analogue to digital (A/D) inputs, three counters and a universal asynchronous receiver/transmitter (UART) for communicating with a PC - but not at the same time. Each A/D input reduces by one the number of I/O pins and by an extra one if there is a need to measure anything other than 0-5V. The UART takes two I/O pins. The counters also use pins, but Timer 0 uses the same pin that one of the A/D inputs uses. So a 16F73 PIC with just one A/D input that measures 0-1V, one 16 bit counter and a communications channel has

18-pin and 28-pin
PIC chips

1

only 15 digital I/O pins and these are organised as 3 bits, 4 bits and 8 bits. This means that the PIC cannot switch all of the I/O pins at the same time. Therefore, some care must be taken over chip type selection.

There are also differences in maximum oscillator speed and maximum program size. The 16F84, for example, has a maximum oscillator speed of 4MHz whereas the 16F84A will operate up to 20MHz. Both chips have only 1024 words of program memory, whilst the 16F628 provides similar capabilities and it has double the program memory.

However, to put these memory sizes into context, none of the projects in this book use more than 512 words of program memory or more than 20 bytes of RAM.

Another factor to remember is that PIC type numbers that contain the letter 'C', such as the 16C54, may be cheaper than those that contain the letter 'F' but they can only be programmed once. Chips that use the letter 'F' in their type number, such as the 16F84, can be erased and reprogrammed many times.

Finally, there are differences in the algorithm (or formula) that is used to program the chips. Therefore, it is important to check that you have the tools to program the type of chip that you are intending to use.

Programming the PIC

Before they can be used, PIC chips must be programmed. Although it is sometimes possible to buy ready programmed chips, the process that is used for programming a chip is:

1. The program is written on a computer such as a PC, and saved as a text file using a text editor such as Notepad or a specialised programming tool. Alternatively it may be possible to load a pre-written text file, that contains the appropriate program, from a web site or from another source.

2. A program that is known as a Compiler or as an Assembler is run on the computer and the text file containing the program is fed into it. The compiler/assembler outputs an object or hexadecimal (hex) file. Again, it may be possible to load a pre-compiled file that contains the appropriate program from a web site or from another source.

3. The chip is loaded into a programming unit that is connected to the computer, and a loader program is run on the computer. This loads the program into the PIC. It may also be possible to connect the programming unit to the chip without removing it from its circuit.

If you are new to PIC programming, I would recommend that you obtain a complete package of compiler, loader and programmer such as the K8048 from Velleman Electronics. This is available as a simple kit. Alternatively, compilers can be downloaded from the Microchip web site (www.microchip.com) or from Shareware sites.

Loader programs normally come with the programmer or they can be downloaded from Shareware sites on the Internet. Unless you obtain the compiler and loader from the same source, make sure that the intermediate file format that they use is the same. The most common file format is known as Intel Hex but other formats can be found. For example, a loader program called SEND uses a file that contains the character equivalents of the hexadecimal values to be loaded into the PIC chip.

Programming languages

Like computer programs, PIC programs are normally written (or coded) in a language that is easier to understand than the binary ones and zeros that the chip actually uses. The main languages for PIC chips are:

- BASIC
- C
- Assembler

Each language claims its own advantages but each has disadvantages as well. Both BASIC and 'C' are derived from computer languages with the same names. They are designed to be easy to learn and to isolate the programmer from a need to understand the intricacies of the computer hardware. Unfortunately, with a PIC it is necessary to get close to the hardware in order to control it in a time critical manner. Therefore, the programs in this book are given in Assembler code.

The two main assembler based compilers are:

- TASM, a table-driven cross assembler that is produced by Speech Technology Inc of Issaquah in the USA. This program is available as Shareware and it will run in an MS-DOS or any Windows environment. TASM produces files that can be loaded via a program called SEND or via PROGPIC/PROGPIC2.
- MPASMWIN from Microchip Technologies Inc. This program needs a 32 bit Microsoft Windows environment and it produces files that can be loaded via PROGPIC2.

These compilers differ in the way that numbers must be defined. For example, a hexadecimal number such as 0A is defined as $0A in TASM and 0x0A in MPASMWIN. In addition, some compiler commands such as END must be preceded by a dot in TASM. MPASM also has a number of reserved words, which cannot be used in a program. These will generate error messages and must be corrected before the program will compile. However, the error messages vary depending on the word that has been used.

An example

This project can be used for a variety of small projects such as an "On the Air" indicator.

The program flashes one or more LEDs as long as pin 17 is at about +5V. LEDs are connected between pins 6 to 13 and the 0V line. Unless 5 volt LEDs are used, series resistors of about 180 ohms will be required to prevent the LEDs from burning out. If pin 17 is connected to 0V, the LEDs are effectively switched off.

The steps in this example are based on the Velleman K8048 programmer, the software that comes with this programmer and on Microsoft Notepad. It also uses the programmer hardware to test the program. In addition to the programmer and software you will need a 16F84 or 16F84A chip.

Step 1 is to type in the program as shown in **Listing 1.1**, into Notepad:

- The first line starts with a semicolon. This indicates a comment. Comments are used to help make the program more readable but they are not included in the final program.
- Line 2 tells the loader program to configure the PIC for a crystal oscillator with no watchdog timer.

```
;16F84 chip with 4MHz Xtal


              __config 0x3FF9


STATUS      EQU        0x3
PORTA       EQU        0x5
PORTB       EQU        0x6
COUNT1      EQU        0x10
COUNT2      EQU        0x11


            ORG        0x0
            NOP
            NOP
            NOP
            NOP
            NOP


            BSF        STATUS, 5
            MOVLW      0xFF
            MOVWF      PORTA
            CLRF       PORTB
            BCF        STATUS, 5

TIME1       MOVLW      0xC8
            MOVWF      COUNT1
TIME2       MOVLW      0xA6
            MOVWF      COUNT2
TIME3       DECFSZ     COUNT2, F
            GOTO       TIME3
            NOP
            NOP
            DECFSZ     COUNT1, F
            GOTO       TIME2
            COMF       PORTB, F
            BTFSS      PORTA, 0
            CLRF       PORTB
            GOTO       TIME1


            END
```

Listing 1.1: An "On the Air" indicator

- Lines 3 to 7 allow the programmer to assign names instead of remembering lots of numbers. For example, the PIC identifies port B as being register number 6 and chips often have more than 50 internal registers in addition to any that the programmer may use. In this example, the status and both the port registers are internal to the PIC and are used for fixed purposes. The count registers are programmer defined.

- Line 8 states that the program should start at location zero and the NOP (no operation) instructions take the program away from areas that are used to handle any interrupts.

- Lines 14 to 18 change the status of the PIC so that port directions can be set. Port A is set to be an input. This is done by loading it with the value of 'FF' (= binary 11111111). Port B is cleared (loaded with all zeros) to set it as an output port. Then, the status is changed back to normal operation.

- Lines 19 to 32 form the actual program. First, register 10 (which has been called 'count1') is loaded with the value C8 hexadecimal (200 decimal). Then register 11 (count2) is loaded with A6 (166). Now we enter a loop where register 11 is decremented by one until it reaches zero. In microseconds, this will take 166 times 3 times cycle time 1/f (where f is the crystal frequency divided by 4). A 4MHz crystal divided by 4 is 1MHz and this gives a cycle time 1/f of 1μs. 166 x 3 x 1μs is 498μs. Two NOPs follow. These do nothing but use up time - 1μs each and this brings the total to 500μs. At the end of the 500μs loop, register 10 is decremented by one and register 11 is reloaded with the value of 166. Thus, the 500μs will be repeated 200 times and this gives a delay of one tenth of a second. The 'comf' instruction changes the state of port B to be the opposite of what is was so, if the lights were out, they are now switched on. Then the program checks the state of pin 17 (port A bit zero). If it is set (+5V) it skips the next instruction and picks up the 'goto'. This starts the program running again by jumping to the location that has been called 'time1'. If the switch is not set (0V) the next instruction is executed and this clears the LEDs on port B.

- Line 33 simply tells the compiler that this is the end of the program.

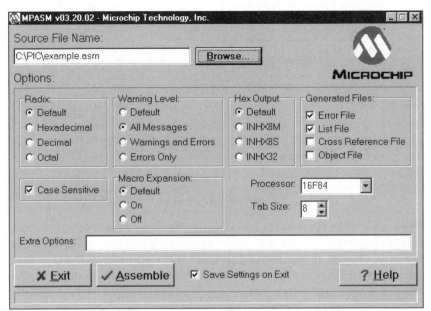

Fig 1.1: MPASMWIN Main Window. Selecting the program

Note that some lines are indented. This is important although it doesn't matter how far they are indented. Any line that is not indented is either a comment (if it starts with a semicolon), a compiler command such as an assignment or a location name. Names cannot contain spaces. So a name of 'time1' is good but 'time 1' would not work.

After typing in the program, save it. It will help the compilation process if you save it with a name that ends in '.asm' although this is not essential. Notepad can be closed at this point although, once again, this is not essential. Indeed, it may be helpful to keep it open so that any mistakes can be corrected.

Now, open the compiler (MPASMWIN). In the 'Processor' box (**see Fig 1.1**), select the correct chip type (16F84 or 16F84A) and browse for the file that you saved earlier. Press the 'Assemble' button. If the program was typed in correctly, a message saying 'Assembly Successful' will be displayed and no Warnings will be reported (**Fig 1.2**).

Should one or more errors occur, the message will say 'Errors Found' (**Fig 1.3**). In this case, look in the folder where you saved the text file and you should

(left) **Fig 1.2: Successful assembly**

(right) **Fig 1.3: Errors found**

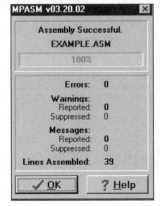
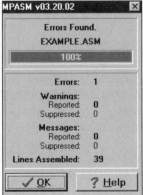

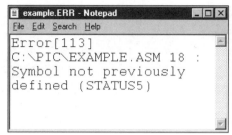

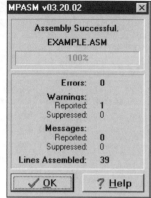

Fig 1.4: The error file

Fig 1.5: Compiler warning

find a file with the same name but ending in '.err'. Open this file with Notepad or a similar text editor and it will tell you what the problem was (**Fig 1.4**). In this case, I mistyped the command BSF STATUS, 5 as BSF STATUS5, 5 on line 18 of the program. Note that in calculating line numbers, the compiler includes any completely blank lines.

You should also note that the compiler will try to correct any errors that it finds. So if I had mistyped the BSF STATUS, 5 command as BSF STATUS, 55 the compiler would have 'corrected' the bit number, but incorrectly to seven (as it would have taken the last three bits from the binary number for 55). This would have resulted in the program failing to run. Therefore warnings, as well as errors, should be corrected before you can say that the program has compiled successfully. The compiler warning and its error report can be seen in **Figs 1.5 and 1.6**.

Once the program has been successfully compiled, it can be loaded into the chip. Place the chip into the programmer and connect the programmer to the PC and a power supply.

Switch the programmer to program mode. Load 'progpic2' into the PC (**Fig 1.7**).

On the File menu, open the file that was compiled. This will have the same basic name as the original file but with a '.hex' ending. On the Port menu, ensure that the correct PC port has a tick against it. Also ensure that there are ticks in all of the

Fig 1.6: Error report for a compiler warning

Fig 1.7: Progpic 2 main window

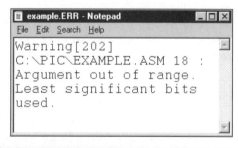

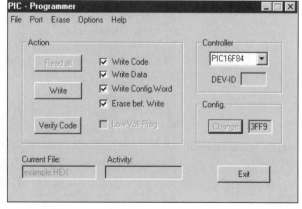

check boxes and that the correct PIC type is selected in the 'Controller' box. Press the 'Write' button and Progpic2 should program the chip.

Various error messages are possible (**Figs 1.8 and 1.9**). K8048 not found could indicate a connection problem between the programmer and the PC, such as the wrong port selected. Note that the programmer is not particularly speed dependant so the port can be set to almost any speed. If there is any doubt, set the port to 9600bps and the programmer to 'normal' speed in the options menu.

No ID received or Write Error indicates that the PIC could not be found or programmed. Check that the PIC is correctly inserted and that the connection cable between the programmer and the PC has all of the correct connection wires. The programmer does not use the data lines of this interface, only the control signals. When the Activity box gives an 'OK' report, the chip is programmed.

If you are using the Velleman programmer, simply move the switch to the Run position and ensure that both JP3 and JP4 are inserted. Press switch SW1 and the LEDs (LD1 to LD6) should flash rapidly.

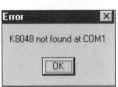

Fig 1.8: Incorrect switch position or bad/wrong chip

Fig 1.9: Incorrectly connected programmer

Velleman programmer

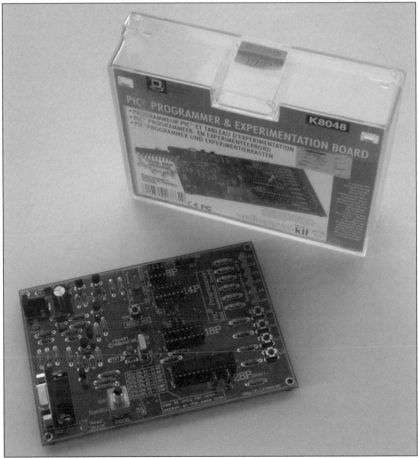

You have now programmed and tested the PIC.

Alternatives

The switch can be reversed, so the lights flash when pin 17 is at 0V, by changing the BTFSS instruction to a BTFSC (**Listing 1.2**).

This causes the program to clear the register if the bit is set, or to skip the clear instruction if the bit is clear.

```
DECFSZ      COUNT1, F
GOTO        TIME2
COMF        PORTB, F
BTFSC       PORTA, 0
CLRF        PORTB
GOTO        TIME1
```

Listing 1.2: Changes for inverted switch

2

Understanding the PIC

The most important part of the PIC is the bank of Registers (see the block diagram in **Fig 2.1**). These provide the link between the program and the real functionality of the chip. So, if you want to change the state of pins 6 to 13 (port B) of a 16F84 chip, you must move some data into register 6. To read the counter/timer, you must look at register 1. Sometimes, you must change more than one register to achieve your result, or even just to access the register you want. For example, to change the pins on port B from input pins to output pins (or vice versa) you must first access register 3 (the status register) and then access register 6. You must also remember to change register 3 back before you can access the data from port B.

There are also some registers that are not connected to other parts of the chip but which are used to keep intermediate calculations that your program makes. For example, in the 16F84, there are 68 registers that are numbered from 0C to 4F hexadecimal. However, these numbers vary between chip types. The 16F73 uses registers 1E and 1F for its analogue to digital (A/D) converter and numbers the general purpose registers from 20 to 7F.

One more register exists. This is known as the 'W' register and it is used to hold information that is currently being worked with. For example, to read the result of an A/D conversion and write it to port B the program must move register 1F to the W register and then move the W register to register 6.

All of these registers are read, written to and generally manipulated by the Arithmetic/Logic Unit (ALU) and this is directly controlled by your program. It executes your program, starting with the instruction in program memory location zero and then in sequential locations unless it is told to do otherwise. There is one exception to this rule. Some events, such as a counter overflowing, an A/D conversion finishing or the signal on a pin changing state, can be allowed to interrupt your program. In this case, the ALU remembers where it was when it was inter-

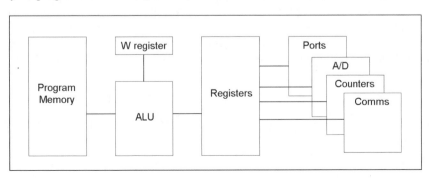

Fig 2.1: PIC Block Diagram

rupted and then it picks up the instruction at location 4 (for a 16F84 chip, but this does vary between chip types). It is then up to your program to handle this interruption before returning to the original point at which it was interrupted.

Numbers

To work in detail with PIC chips it is also necessary to understand a little about binary systems.

For binary systems, the only thing that matters is whether a signal is off or on. There is no such thing as being half on. A single wire, carrying a binary signal, is called a 'bit'. Complex signals are formed either by switching the signal on and off several times or by using multiple wires.

Two wires (two bits) can have four states:
- Both wires off
- Wire 2 off and wire 1 on - actually, a real programmer would call them bit 1 and bit 0
- Wire 2 on and wire 1 off (bit 1 on & bit 0 off)
- Both wires on (both bits on)

Three wires (three bits) can have eight states:
- All bits off
- Bit 2 off, bit 1 off, bit 0 on
- Bit 2 off, bit 1 on, bit 0 off
- Bit 2 off, bit 1 on, bit 0 on
- Bit 2 on, bit 1 off, bit 0 off
- Bit 2 on, bit 1 off, bit 0 on
- Bit 2 on, bit 1 on, bit 0 off
- All bits on.

Each additional bit doubles the number of combinations, so:
- 4 bits have 16 combinations
- 5 bits have 32 combinations
- 6 bits have 64 combinations
- 7 bits have 128 combinations
- 8 bits have 256 combinations
- 10 bits have 1024 combinations
- 16 bits have 65536 combinations
- 24 bits have 16777216 combinations

By giving bits a value other than one, these values can be achieved.

For example, a value of 10 is implemented on four or more bits with a combination of on, off, on, off (or 1010). Just looking at the 'on' bits (or logic ones) in **Fig 2.2**, eight plus two is ten. However, using this system, the maximum value is one less than the number of combinations. This is because one of the combinations (all off) is used for the value of zero.

BIT	7	6	5	4	3	2	1	0
	128	64	32	16	8	4	2	1

Fig 2.2: Binary numbers

However, it is important to realise that this numbering system is purely in the mind of the programmer. The PIC itself thinks only in terms of signals that are on or off. In some cases, such as when adding and subtracting numbers, it also thinks that the next higher bit is worth twice this bit and that the next lower number is worth half of this bit. For example, the binary number of 00001010 could be worth 10 or it could be worth 80 (64 + 16) if it is the top 8 bits of a 10 bit number (and the last two bits were zero). In this case, the full binary number of 0000101000 is split over two registers with one register containing the most significant 8 bits and the other register holding the bottom two bits. The 16F873 chip contains a ten bit Analogue to Digital (A/D) converter. This must split the eight bits between two registers but it can either place the top or the bottom two bits in one register whilst the other eight bits go into another register. A number of PIC chips also contain 16 bit counters. If the count is 2560 and the reading is split across two 8 bit registers, one would contain 00001010 (in this case, the bits are worth 2048 and 512) and the other would contain zero.

Another important factor is the way that the PIC handles results that extend beyond 8 bits. For example, if 8 (00001000) is added to 250 (11111010), the result is 2. This is because the register can only hold 256 combinations of numbers and so 256 is effectively subtracted from the result. The carry bit is set to show that this has been done. Similarly, if 12 is subtracted from 4, the result is 248.

This raises the issue of negative numbers. Bearing in mind that the PIC itself only works with ones and zeros, programmers can consider 248 to be exactly the same as minus 8. This inverted logic treats the zeros as being significant and the minimum value as being minus one. Thus, binary 11111111 is minus one, 11111110 is minus two and 11111101 is minus three. Although this could be taken to the extreme of considering 00000000 to be minus 256, such an approach would be unusual. A more common approach is to consider all numbers of 127 (01111111) or lower as positive and numbers of 128 (1000000) and above to be negative - or should I have said minus 127 (1000000). In this case, the most significant (or left hand) bit becomes a sign bit - 0 and the number is positive, 1 and it is negative. However, with this approach, 96 plus 96 becomes minus 64 rather than plus 192 and the carry bit will not be set. So the programmer must ensure that there is no scope for confusion.

It may be that the number cannot go above 127 or it may be necessary to test bit 7, ensuring that it is not set after an addition and that it is set after a subtraction.

Hexadecimal

Another trick used by programmers when representing numbers, is to count in hexadecimal (or hex). Hex simply counts up to 15, which is the maximum number that four bits can hold. Although this may seem like an added burden when working with small numbers, it can pay dividends with larger numbers. For example, with a number such as 57344 it is not easy to see which bits are set but if the number is written as E000 than it is easy to see that the bottom 12 bits are all off (000). From the hex numbers in **Listing 2.1**, it can be seen that the top three bits are on and bit 12 is off. Of course, it takes practice to learn this.

Listing 2.1: Hexadecimal numbers

Bits	Decimal	Hex
0000	0	0
0001	1	1
0010	2	2
0011	3	3
0100	4	4
0101	5	5
0110	6	6
0111	7	7
1000	8	8
1001	9	9
1010	10	A
1011	11	B
1100	12	C
1101	13	D
1110	14	E
1111	15	F

Numbers and compilers

Differing compilers require number types to be identified differently:

Type	TASM	MPASM
Binary	1011b or %1011	B'1011'
Decimal	13d or just plain 13	D'13' or .13
Hexadecimal	0DH or $0D	0x0D or H'0D' or just plain 0D

Note that the instruction 'ADDLW 25' will add 25 to the W register if the program is compiled under TASM but it will add 37 (25 hex) if the program is compiled under MPASM. Therefore I would strongly recommend that you explicitly specify the type for all numbers that you use.

Registers

The exact number of registers will vary depending on the type of PIC (see **Table 2.1**). For example, the 16F84 has about 16 registers whilst some 16F873 chips have about 55. These registers are organised in a number of banks and the status register must be changed to select the required bank. Some registers are

Table 2.1: PIC Registers

Register number		Bank 0	Bank 1	Bank 2	Bank 3
00	INDR	Indirect Data	Indirect Data	Indirect Data	Indirect Data
01		Timer 0	Options	Timer 0	Options
02	PCL	Prog Counter Low	Prog Counter Low	Prog Counter Low	Prog Counter Low
03		Status	Status	Status	Status
04	FSR	Indirect Address	Indirect Address		
05		PORT A data	PORT A Direction		
06		PORT B data	PORT B Direction	PORT B data	PORT B Direction
07		PORT C data	PORT C Direction		
08		PORT D data	PORT D Direction		
09		PORT E data	PORT E Direction		
0A	PCLATH	Prog Counter High	Prog Counter High	Prog Counter High	Prog Counter High
0B		Interrupt Control	Interrupt Control	Interrupt Control	Interrupt Control
0C		Interrupt Flags 1	Interrupt Enables 1	Prog Read Data Low	Program Read Contrl
0D		Interrupt Flage 2	Interrupt Enables 2	Prog Read Add Low	
0E		Timer 1 Low	Power Control	Prog Read Data High	
0F		Timer 1 High		Prog Read Add High	
10		Timer 1 Control		User Data	User Data
11		Timer 2 Data		User Data	User Data
12		Timer 2 Control	Timer 2 Period	User Data	User Data
13		Sync Serial TX/RX	Sync Serial Address	User Data	User Data
14		Sync Serial Control	Sync Serial Statistics	User Data	User Data
15		Compare 1 Low		User Data	User Data
16		Compare 1 High		User Data	User Data
17		Compare 1 Control		User Data	User Data
18		UART RX Control	UART TX Control	User Data	User Data
19		UART RX Data	UART Baud Rate	User Data	User Data
1A		UART TX Data		User Data	User Data
1B		Compare 2 Low		User Data	User Data
1C		Compare 2 High		User Data	User Data
1D		Compare 2 Control		User Data	User Data
1E		A/D Data		User Data	User Data
1F		A/D Control 1	A/D Control 2	User Data	User Data

Notes: *Some registers may not be available on some chip types or on some pin configurations.*
Where a register does not contain any details, it cannot be used.
The user data registers are only available on some chip types.

available in more than one bank but others will only be available when a specific bank is selected.

To select a bank, change bits 5 and 6 of the status register:
- Both bits cleared (00)   bank 0
- Bit 6 cleared and bit 5 set (01)   bank 1
- Bit 6 set and bit 5 cleared (10)   bank 2
- Both bits set (11)   bank 3

When the PIC is powered up, bank 0 will be automatically selected.

User registers

In addition to the registers that control the internal functions of the PIC, each chip has a number of general purpose registers that programmers can use in their user applications. The number and location of these registers varies between chip types. For example, the 16F84 has 68 user registers that are numbered from 0C to 2F hexadecimal whereas the 16F873 has 336 user registers that are numbered from 20 to 7F hexadecimal in bank zero and 20 to 6F hexadecimal in the other three register banks.

Indirect access to registers

There are times when you may wish to calculate the register number. For example, many projects store a number of characters in consecutive user registers. When these registers are updated, the program must calculate the address of the character that is being changed. To achieve this, the registers must be accessed indirectly. The register number (address) is placed into register 4 (the FSR register). Once this has been done, register zero (the INDR register) becomes the register that you are accessing. For example, if the value 3 is placed in the FSR register, the status register can be changed either by accessing register 3 as normal, or by accessing register zero. If the value in register 4 is changed to 6, register zero now contains the data for Port B.

The code in **Listing 2.2** is taken from the clock project and sends consecutive characters to Port B. Note that CHAR is a user register that contains the character number, and the characters are in registers 10 to 17 hexadecimal.

Register bank 1 is accessed by adding hexadecimal 80 to the register number so the Port B direction register, which is normally register 6 of bank 1, is accessed by placing the value 86 into the FSR register and the using the INDR register to read or set the directions. Bank 2 is accessed by setting bit 7 of the status register. To access register bank 3 both bit 7 of the status register must be set and hex 80 must be added to the register number. Remember to clear bit 7 of the status register to access register banks 0 and 1. Bit 7 of the status register is only used when accessing registers indirectly. To access the registers directly, bits 5 and 6 of the status registers must be manipulated.

```
INCF      CHAR, W     ;Update character number
ADDLW     0x10        ;Add hexadecimal 10
MOVWF     FSR         ;Move into FSR register
MOVF      INDR, W     ;Read data from INDR register
MOVWF     PORTB       ;Write data to Port B
```

Listing 2.2: Writing to Port B

Instructions

Sources and destinations for data

The ALU can obtain its data from:

- The Registers
- The W register
- Part of the program instruction. For example, ADDLW 0x25 will add hexadecimal 25 to the W register. This is known as a Literal.

For many instructions, such as an addition, the ALU will need to obtain data from two sources. However it should be noted that the ALU can not get data from a register (except for the W register) and a literal at the same time. To add a literal to a register, other than the W register, the literal must first be moved into the W register and then the W register can be added to the other register.

Once the ALU has completed its function, the result can be placed:

- In the W register
- In another register.

However, if any of the data came from a register, the result can only be placed back in the same register. This means that it is not possible to move data from register 5 to register 6 in a single instruction. It must first be moved from register 5 to the W register and then moved from the W register to register 6.

Remember that the ALU works on 8 bits at a time and that, unless a register or bit is explicitly changed, it will stay as it is. This means that if the first instruction sets the carry bit in the status register, no matter how many other instructions are executed, if none of them affect the carry bit it will remain set until the end of the program. In addition, a value in the W register will remain in the W register until it is overwritten, no matter how many times it is written to somewhere else or used in calculations where the result is not written to the W register.

Instructions that work with two numbers

The following types of instruction work with the contents of the W register and either a literal or the contents of another register.

Add. A literal can be added to the contents of the W register and place the result in the W register (ADDLW), or the contents of the W register can be added to a register (ADDWF). The result of an ADDWF instruction can be placed back into the same register than one of the numbers came from or it can be placed onto the W register. Bits in the status register may be set as a result of an addition. The Carry bit (register 3 bit 0) will be set if the result is more than 255, and 256 will be subtracted from the result. So, for example, 192 plus 192 equals 128 (384-256) with the carry bit set to a logic one. The Digit Carry bit will be set if the sum of the bottom four bits in each number adds up to more than 16. For example, adding 12 and 12 will give a result of 24 and the digit carry bit will be set to a logic one. The zero bit will be set if the result of the addition is exactly 256. This is because the PIC is unable to tell whether you are working with positive or negative numbers.

Subtract. There are two subtract instructions. SUBLW subtracts the contents of the W register from the literal value declared in your instruction and SUBWF subtracts the contents of the W register from the contents of another register. It is not possible to subtract anything from the W register. With the SUBWF instruction, the result can be placed either in the W register or in the register that the other number was obtained from. Subtract instructs can also modify the Carry, Digit Carry and Zero bits. The zero bit will be set to a logic one only if the result is exactly zero. Carry and digit carry will be set if the result is less than zero and, in this case, 256 will be added to the result. Note that the PIC does not know whether you are working with full eight bit bytes or with hexadecimal digits so it sets both bits in the status register.

AND is a logical function that sets a bit in the output only if the same bit is set in both of the inputs. Once again, you can AND the W register with either a literal or with another register. If one of the numbers came from a register then you can place the result back in the same register. Alternatively, you can place the result into the W register. The zero bit will be set if there are no cases where the same bit is set in both numbers.

OR (Inclusive OR) is a logical function that sets a bit in the output if the same bit is set in either or both of the inputs. There is no carry between the bits, so 00000001 'OR'ed with 00000001 will give a result of 00000001. (An ADD will give 00000010). You can OR the W register with either a literal or another register. If one of the numbers came from a register then you can place the result back in the same register. Alternatively, you can place the result into the W register. The zero bit will be set if both numbers are zero to start with.

Exclusive OR (XOR) is a logical function that sets a bit in the output if the same bit is set in either of the inputs but not in both. So 0 exclusive 'OR'ed with 0 is 0, 0 exclusive 'OR'ed with 1 is 1 and 1 exclusive 'OR'ed with 1 is 0. Once again, you can and the W register with either a literal or another register. If one of the numbers came from a register then you can place the result back in the same register. Alternatively, you can place the result into the W register. The zero bit will be set if the result is all zeros.

Instructions that work with a single number

Clear clears the specified register and sets the zero bit (bit 2) in the status register (register 3) to a logic one.

Move moves either:
- A literal part of the instruction to the W register (MOVLW)
- The contents of the W register to a specified register (MOVWF)
- The contents of a specified register to either the W register or back to itself (MOVF). The MOVF is the only one of these three instructions that will change the zero bit of the status register.

Increment and Decrement. These instructions increment (INCF will add one to) or decrement (DECF will subtract one from) a specified register which can not be the W register. To change the contents of the W register use ADDLW 1 or SUBLW 1. All of these instructions will set the zero bit in the status register if the result is zero or 256. However, if the result is 256 it will not set the carry bit.

Rotate. The contents of the specified register are moved one bit to the left (RLF) or right (RRF). The bit that would otherwise be lost is placed into the carry bit of the status register and the contents of the carry bit are placed in the vacant bit. RLF is the equivalent of multiplying by two with overflow carry and with the insertion of the result of a previous overflow. RRF is equivalent to dividing by two, again with carry bit manipulation. It is not possible to rotate the W register.

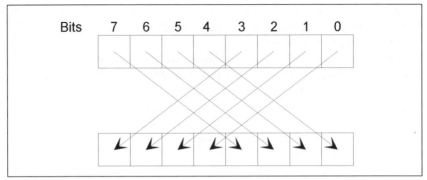

Swap Nibbles. Bits 0 to 3 of a register are swapped with bits 4 to 7 of the same register (see **Fig 2.3**) and the result is either placed in the W register or it is placed back in the same register that the data was obtained from. It is not possible to swap the nibbles of the W register.

Bit Set and Bit Clear. These instructions can set and clear individual bits in a register. It is not possible to manipulate bits in the W register.

Program flow instructions

GOTO. This instruction moves the program counter so that it picks up and executes instruction starting at the address specified in the instruction. The GOTO instruction that the PIC executes specifies a numeric address, but the compiler allows you to use a name. This name is then placed, as a label, on the left hand side of the instruction that you wish to go to. This allows you to modify the program without having to recalculate all of the GOTO and CALL instructions. Note that GOTO instructions will only go to instructions within a 2048 location block of memory. Special techniques are needed if the jump is outside this block.

CALL and RETURN (see **Fig 2.4**). The main difference between a CALL and a GOTO instruction is that the PIC remembers the address that the call was made from. When a return instruction is executed, the PIC returns to the calling address, then executes the next instruction. There are two types of return. RETFIE simply returns whilst RETLW loads an explicit value into the W register before returning. With the RETFIE instruction, if there is a value in the W register then it stays in the W register. It should also be noted that any changes made whilst in the call routine (or subroutine) will remain changed when the program returns to the calling instruction. This includes any status bits, so if the zero bit was set before the call and an add instruction in the subroutine resets the zero bit to zero; the zero bit will be zero after the return. The PIC will continue to remember the calling address until

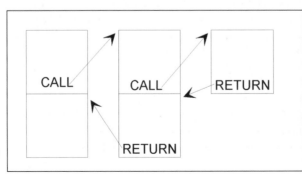

it encounters a return instruction, when it will forget it. This means that sub-routines can contain GOTO and similar flow control instructions. The can even contain call instructions. If calls are nested in this way, the PIC will return to the most recently issued calling address. Up to 6 nested addresses can be remembered by the PIC.

Skip if Zero. Increment/decrement instructions can be modified by adding SZ to them. So INCF becomes INCFSZ and DECF becomes DECFSZ. If the result of the increment is 256, or if the result of the decrement is zero, the next instruction is skipped and the one after that is executed. Often the intermediate instruction will be a GOTO instruction. For example, the routine in **Fig 2.5** provides a time delay. In this example, a register called REG1 is cleared. It is then decremented so that it now contains 255 (-1). Because it no longer contains zero, the next instruction is executed. That passes control back to the decrement instruction, which subtracts another one (254). This loop continues, with the register being decremented by one each time, until the register contains zero. At this point, the GOTO is skipped and the following instruction executed.

Fig 2.5: A time delay loop

Skip if Bit Set or Clear. It is also possible to test an individual bit in any register except for the W register and to skip the next instruction if it is set to a one (BTFSS) or cleared to a zero (BTFSC). For example, BTFSS 3, 2 will test the zero bit in the status register and execute the next instruction if the zero bit is not set (ie the result of the calculation is not zero). This instruction will be skipped and the following instruction executed if the bit is set because the calculation resulted in zero.

BTFSS 3,2
;Result not zero
;Result is zero

Miscellaneous instructions

NOP. No operation. It does nothing but uses time. It is a very useful instruction for trimming and extending timing loops.

CLRWDT. This instruction clears the watchdog timer counter back to its starting position. The watchdog timer is a timer that can be enabled and used either as a timer or as a software failsafe. As a timer, it is not very accurate because it uses a resistor and capacitor to provide the timing and these are very temperature sensitive. However, it can be set for times varying from less than 20ms to over 2.3 seconds. If this timer expires, it causes an interrupt. A common use for the watchdog timer, in applications where the PIC cannot easily be reset, is as a trap for software glitches. Whilst the software is running, it issues regular CLTWDT commands. Should the software encounter a problem, these instructions will not be issued and the Watchdog will cause an interrupt.

Sleep. This instruction causes the PIC to stop executing instructions and to go into a low power mode until it encounters an interrupt. Interrupts can come from multiple sources, such as timers overflowing, conversions finishing, communications resources filling up or emptying, as well as from the watchdog.

	Bit	Set	Clear	Test
Table 2.2: Bit equivalents	0	IORLW 0x01	ANDLW 0xFE	ANDLW 0x01
	1	IORLW 0x02	ANDLW 0xFD	ANDLW 0x02
	2	IORLW 0x04	ANDLW 0xFB	ANDLW 0x04
	3	IORLW 0x08	ANDLW 0xF7	ANDLW 0x08
	4	IORLW 0x10	ANDLW 0xEF	ANDLW 0x10
	5	IORLW 0x20	ANDLW 0xDF	ANDLW 0x20
	6	IORLW 0x40	ANDLW 0xBF	ANDLW 0x40
	7	IORLW 0x80	ANDLW 0x7F	ANDLW 0x80

Manipulating data in the W register

Sometimes a program finds that data in the W register needs to be manipulated, and that the appropriate instructions only work when data is in a user register. Examples include complement (COMF), increment and decrement (INCF and DECF), increment/decrement and skip if zero (DECFSZ), bit test (BTFSS and BTFSC) and bit set/clear (BSF and BCF).

However, there are ways of manipulating the W register that achieve the same results:

- XORLW 0xFF   is the same as complement W.
- SUBLW 0x01   is the same as decrement W
- ADDLW 0x01   is the same as increment W
- IORLW   is the same as bit set
- ANDLW   is the same as bit clear

To set or clear a bit, the W register must be 'OR'ed or 'AND'ed with the appropriate number as in **Table 2.2**. This approach can also be used to test a bit, as long as you remember that it will destroy the data in the W register. First, the W register is 'AND'ed with the appropriate number for the bit that you want to test. Then, execute a BTFSS STATUS, ZERO or BTFSC STATUS, ZERO instruction. Remember that the zero bit will be set if the bit to be tested is clear.

Executing a BTFSS or BTFSC instruction on the zero bit of the status register can also be used after an ADDLW or SUBLW to turn these into skip on zero commands.

Multiplying

There is no multiply instruction in the PIC instruction set. However, the same result can be achieved either by adding a number to itself, or by a combination of shift and add.

```
        CLRF      RESULT          ;Clear results register
        MOVF      B, F            ;Check if B already zero
        BTFSC     STATUS, ZERO
        RETURN
LOOP    MOVF      A, W
        ADDWF     RESULT, F       ;Add A to result
        DECFSZ    B, F            ;Decrement B
        RETURN                    ;Return if end
        GOTO      LOOP            ;Continue if not end
```

Listing 2.3: Add method of multiplying

For example, if the two numbers to be multiplied are in register 'A' and register 'B'. The result is placed in a register called 'RESULT':

Although the add method looks simpler than the shift method it can be a lot slower. This is because it has to cycle through the loop up to 256 times whereas the loop method only cycles 8 times.

Both of these examples (**Listings 2.3 and 2.4**) will only work if the result is less than 256. Otherwise, two registers will be needed. The example in **Listing 2.5** multiplies two 8 bit numbers to produce high and low bytes that make up the results.

The shift method of multiplying needs an extra register to hold A as it is shifted. This extra register is called 'C' (see **Listing 2.6**).

Both these methods will multiply two bytes together and produce a product with a value of up to 65535.

Division

There is no easy way to divide numbers with a PIC. So 250/5 = ? The easiest way to achieve the same result is to turn the question around and ask "how many times do I have to multiply the 5 to get 250.

```
        CLRF     RESULTS               ;Clear results register
        MOVLW    0x08                  ;Set number of cycles
        MOVWF    COUNT
LOOP    BTFSS    A, 0                  ;Check if relevant bit of A set
        GOTO     SKIP                  ;No
        MOVF     B, W                  ;Yes so add shifted B to results
        ADDWF    RESULTS, F
SKIP    RRF      A                     ;Shift A right
        RLF      B                     ;Shift B left
        DECFSZ   COUNT                 ;Is it the end
        RETURN                         ;Yes
        GOTO     LOOP                  ;No
```

Listing 2.4: Shift method of multiplying

```
        CLRF     RESULTL               ;Clear low 8 bits of results register
        CLRF     RESULTH               ;Clear high 8 bits of results register
        MOVF     B, F                  ;Check if B already zero
        BTFSC    STATUS, ZERO
        RETURN
LOOP    MOVF     A, W
        ADDWF    RESULTL, F            ;Add A to result
        BTFSC    STATUS, CARRY         ;Check if carry bit set
        INCF     RESULTH, F            ;Yes so increment results high reg.
        DECFSZ   B, F                  ;Decrement B
        RETURN                         ;Return if end
        GOTO     LOOP                  ;Continue if not end
```

Listing 2.5: Add method of multiplying multiple bytes

```
            CLRF        RESULTL         ;Clear low 8 bits of results register
            CLRF        RESULTH         ;Clear high 8 bits of results register
            CLRF        C
            MOVLW       0x08
            MOVWF       COUNT
LOOP        BTFSS       A, 0            ;Check if relevant bit of A set
            GOTO        SKIP            ;No
            MOVF        B, W            ;Yes so add shifted B to results
            ADDWF       RESULTL, F
            BTFSC       STATUS, CARRY   ;Is result more than 255
            INCF        RESULTH, F      ;Yes so increment high result
            MOVF        C, W
            ADDWF       RESULTH, F
SKIP        RRF         A               ;Shift A right
            RLF         B               ;Shift B left
            RLF         C               ;Shift C left
            DECFSZ      COUNT           ;Is it the end
            RETURN                      ;Yes
            GOTO        LOOP            ;No
```

Listing 2.6: Shift method of multiplying multiple bytes

If the program is working with 8 bit numbers, the procedure is as follows:
- Multiply the lower number by 128.
- Check if the total is higher or lower that the higher number.
- If the total is lower or the same, add 128 number to the results register and subtract the total from the higher number.
- If the total is higher, add nothing to the results register and do not subtract anything from the higher number
- Repeat this procedure with 64, 32, 16, 8, 4, 2 and 1.

With the above figures of 250/5:
- 5 times 128 is 640. This is higher than 250 so take no action.
- 5 times 64 is 320. This is higher than 250 so take no action.
- 5 times 32 is 160. This is lower than 250 so add 64 to result and subtract 160 from 250 to leave 90.
- 5 times 16 is 80. This is lower than 250 so add 32 to result and subtract 80 from 90 to leave 10.
- 5 times 8 is 40. This is higher than 10 so take no action.
- 5 times 4 is 20. This is higher than 10 so take no action.
- 5 times 2 is 10. This is the same as 10 so add 2 to result and subtract 10 from 10 to leave zero.
- 5 times 1 is 5. This is higher than zero, so take no action.

The result register contains 64 plus 16 plus 2, which equals 50 and 250/5 also equals 50. It should be noted that this method will always round down when an exact division is not possible.

Greater than and less than

It is easy to find out if two numbers are the same. Either exclusive OR them together or subtract one from the other. If the result is zero then they are the same. To find the higher number, the first thing to do is to check whether these figures are more or less than 128 by checking whether bit 7 is set in each number. If bit 7 is set in one number and not the other then one number is clearly higher than the other. When bit 7 is set in both numbers then clear it in both numbers. Now subtract one number from the other. If bit 7 is set in the result then the subtracted number is higher than the other number.

For example, if register A and B contain values, use **Listing 2.7**.

Long jumps and calculated jumps

Because the Program Counter, which holds the address of the next instruction to be executed, can be smaller than the amount of memory in some chip types, special techniques are needed when program control must be passed beyond this barrier. The normal program counter is 11 bits long and this means that it can count from zero to 2047. Some chips have a program memory that can hold up to 4096 instructions. This means that GOTO and CALL instructions will not work between the lower and upper halves of memory.

In these cases, you must calculate the address to be jumped to and load it into the registers yourself. The upper 5 bits go into register 0A hexadecimal in any bank and the lower 8 bits go into register 2 of any register bank. The jump will take effect as soon as you load register 2, so register 0A must be loaded first. However, the reverse of this is that register 0A can be changed long before you need to use it. In addition, if register 0A is read, the contents will not be related to the current instruction address. However, register 2 does contain an up to date address.

It is also possible to calculate jumps on the fly by doing the mathematics and loading the result into register 2 (and register 0A if necessary). For example, the code in **Listings 2.8 and 2.9** converts a number in the range 0 to 9 into ASCII. ASCII is the code that is used by alphanumeric displays. The code comprises a subroutine and the routine that calls the subroutine.

Listing 2.7: Finding the greater number

```
          BTFSS    A, 7            ;Check if bit 7 of A set
          GOTO     A-LO           ;No
          BTFSC    B, 7           ;Bit 7 of A set so check if B also set
          GOTO     BOTHHI         ;Yes so both over 128
          GOTO     A-HI           ;No so A must be higher than B
A-LO      BTFSS    B, 7           ;Bit 7 of A not set so check B
          GOTO     BOTHLO         ;No, both less than 128
          GOTO     B-HI           ;Yes so B must be higher

BOTHHI    BCF      A, 7           ;Both high so subtract 128 from A and B
          BCF      B, 7

BOTHLO    MOVF     A, W           ;Both now less than 128 so,
          SUBWF    B, W           ;Subtract A from B
          ANDLW    0x80           ;Is bit 7 set?
          BTFSS    STATUS, ZERO
          GOTO     A-HI           ;Yes so A must be higher than B
          GOTO     B-HI           ;No so B must be higher that A
```

```
        MOVLW       0x1
        MOVWF       PCLATH          ;PCLATH is register 0A
        MOVF        DATA, W         ;DATA contains number to be converted
        CALL        XTABLE
        MOVWF       ASCII           ;ASCII will receive the ASCII character
```

Listing 2.8: The calling routine

```
        ORG         0x100           ;Tell compiler where to locate this
                                    subroutine
XTABLE  ADDWF       PCL, F
        RETLW       0x30            ;Zero
        RETLW       0x31            ;One
        RETLW       0x32            ;Two
        RETLW       0x33            ;Three
        RETLW       0x34            ;Four
        RETLW       0x35            ;Five
        RETLW       0x36            ;Six
        RETLW       0x37            ;Seven
        RETLW       0x38            ;Eight
        RETLW       0x39            ;Nine
```

Listing 2.9: The subroutine

(Note that the word TABLE or any word starting with TABLE is reserved in MPASM and must not be used in a program. It can, however, be used with TASM)

Because the subroutine is located at an address of hexadecimal 100 (ORG 0x100), the calling routine must first load register 0A (PCLATH) before it calls the table. If this was not done, the call itself would still work. This is because CALL can operate over a 2048 (hex 800) range but the add would then produce the wrong result.

Immediately before calling the subroutine, the W register is loaded with the numeric value (0-9). Once in the subroutine, the contents of the W register are added to the current position. For example, if the number is zero and the table is located at location 0x100, the following will occur:

- Register 2 will contain 00 because it only contains the bottom 8 bits of the location
- W contains 0
- Zero plus zero is zero
- Zero is loaded into register 2
- Because 1 has previously been loaded into register 0A, the program counter now contains 0x100
- Because the instruction is an ADD, the program counter is automatically incremented at the end of the instruction. This means that the program counter now contains 0x101
- The instruction at location 0x101 (RETLW 0x30) loads the value of 0x30 into the W register and returns control to the calling routine
- The next instruction in the calling routine moves the contents of the W register (0x30) into the ASCII register

If the subroutine is located in the lowest 256 words of memory, there is no need to set the PCLATH register (register 0A).

Program memory and EEPROM data

Some PIC types do not have these facilities.

When the PIC is loses power, or is powered down, all information held in the registers is lost. Sometimes, it is nice to keep information from session to session. For example, so that a radio powers back up on the same frequency that it was on when it was switched off.

PICs can provide two different mechanisms for holding this type of data. These are:

- the ability to read and modify program memory
- an area of Electrically Erasable Programmable Read Only Memory (EEPROM)

Note that some chip types have both of these facilities, some have only EEPROM and some have neither. For those that have neither, there is no way to store data within the PIC if it loses power. However, a battery backup may be used to maintain power when other parts of the circuit are powered off.

EEPROM

Chips like the 16F84 have EEPROM memory. The 16F84 has 64 locations and each location can hold 8 bits.

This is accessed through registers 08 and 09 hexadecimal in register banks 0 and 1 (**Fig 2.6**).

The mechanism for storing data in an EEPROM location is fairly complex, takes time and must not be interrupted. Therefore, an EEPROM write must not be undertaken whilst the PIC is executing a critical routine. The process is:

1. Place the address (location) in the address register (register 09 of register bank 0)
2. Place the data in the data register (register 08 of bank 0)
3. Disable all interrupts
4. Set the 'write enable' bit (bit 2) of the Control 1 register (register 8 of bank 1)
5. Write the value of hexadecimal 55 (01010101) to the Control 2 register (register 9 of bank 1)
6. Write the value of hexadecimal AA (10101010) to the Control 2 register (register 9 of bank 1)
7. Set the 'write' bit (bit 1) of the Control 1 register (register 8 of bank 1)
8. Wait until the 'write' bit has been reset by the PIC
9. Clear the write enable bit and enable interrupts if necessary.

For example, the routine in **Listing 2.10** will store an 8 bit frequency in EEPROM location 01 if the frequency is in the W register when this routine is called. Note that the last line is optional.

Because writing to EEPROM can take some time, especially in early PIC chips and in PIC chips that use very fast oscillator clocks, it is also possible to

	Bank 0	Bank 1
0x08	DATA	CONTROL 1
0x09	ADDRESS	CONTROL 2

Fig 2.6: Accessing EEPROM data

```
          MOVWF    0x08           ;Store frequency in register 8
          MOVLW    0x01
          MOVWF    0x09           ;Load EEPROM location (01) in reg 09
          BCF      0x0B, 7        ;Disable Interrupts
          BSF      3, 5           ;Go to register bank 1
          BSF      0x08, 2        ;Set the Write Enable bit
          MOVLW    0x55
          MOVWF    0x09           ;Write '55' to Control 2
          MOVLW    0xAA
          MOVWF    0x09           ;Write 'AA' to Control 2
          BSF      0x08, 1        ;Set the Write bit
LOOP      BTFSC    0x08, 1        ;Check if bit still set
          GOTO     LOOP           ;Loop if still set
          BCF      0x08, 2        ;Clear the Write Enable bit
          BCF      3,5            ;Return to register bank 0
          BSF      0x0B, 7        ;Enable Interrupts if required
```

Listing 2.10: Writing to EEPROM

```
          MOVLW    0x01
          MOVWF    0x09           ;Load EEPROM location (01) in reg 09
          BSF      3, 5           ;Go to register bank 1
          BSF      0x0C, 0        ;Set the Read bit
          BCF      3,5            ;Return to register bank 0
          MOVF     0x08, W        ;Move frequency to W register
```

Listing 2.11: Reading EEPROM data

set up an interrupt. The interrupt is triggered when the write is complete. To set the interrupt, the appropriate bit must be set in either the INTCON register (register 0x0B) or in one of the PIE registers (register 0x0C 0r 0x0D). The exact bit location varies between chip types.

Reading the data back from EEPROM is simpler. It is simply necessary to specify the address and to set the 'read' bit (bit 0) in the control 1 register. The data can then be read from register 8 of bank 0. There is no need to disable interrupts or to wait for the routine to finish. The routine (**Listing 2.11**) shows this. It reads back the frequency from location 1 of EEPROM and places it into the W register.

Fig 2.7: PIC 16F872 access to EEPROMs

Chips like the 16F872 also have EEPROM memory. However, because registers 8 and 9 are used for Port D and Port E, registers 0C and 0D hexadecimal in register banks 2 and 3 are used (**Fig 2.7**).

However, because these registers are also used to access program memory, the additional step of clearing register 0F hexadecimal and of clearing bit 7 of the Control 1 register is needed.

The code segment shown in **Listing 2.12** shows the EEPROM write for a 16F873 chip. The additional lines are in italic type. However,

	Bank 2	Bank 3
0x0C	DATA	CONTROL 1
0x0D	ADDRESS	CONTROL 2

there are also some changes to the order of instructions so that the correct register bank is selected.

Reading the EEPROM also requires some additional instructions and some changes in the order of instructions so that the correct register bank is selected (**Listing 2.13**).

Program memory

The 16F873 and similar chips, also have the ability to read program memory into the registers and to write program memory providing it has not been protected when the chip was programmed.

This allows program memory to hold data, but care must be taken to ensure that it is not executed as instructions. This is probably best done by placing the data area well away from the program

The advantage over EEPROM of using program memory is that program memory is 14 bits wide.

(top) Listing 2.12: Writing to EEPROM on 16F872 Chips

(bottom)   Listing 2.13: Reading the EEPROM on 16F872 Chips

```
        BCF     0x0B, 7     ;Disable Interrupts
        BSF     3, 6        ;Go to bank 2
        MOVWF   0x0C        ;Store frequency in register 0x0C
        CLRF    0x0F        ;Clear the high address register
        MOVLW   0x01
        MOVWF   0x0D        ;Load EEPROM location (01) in reg 0x0D
        BSF     3, 5        ;Go to register bank 3
        BCF     0x08, 7     ;Allow EEPROM access
        BSF     0x08, 2     ;Set the Write Enable bit
        MOVLW   0x55
        MOVWF   0x0D        ;Write '55' to Control 2
        MOVLW   0xAA
        MOVWF   0x0D        ;Write 'AA' to Control 2
        BSF     0x0C, 1     ;Set the Write bit
LOOP    BTFSC   0x0C, 1     ;Check if bit still set
        GOTO    LOOP        ;Loop if still set
        BCF     0x0C, 2     ;Clear the Write Enable bit
        BCF     3,6         ;Return to register bank 2
        BCF     3,5         ;Return to register bank 0
        BSF     0x0B, 7     ;Enable Interrupts if required
```

```
        MOVLW   0x01
        MOVWF   0x0D        ;Load EEPROM location (01) in reg 0x0D
        CLRF    0x0F        ;Clear the high address register
        BSF     3, 6        ;Go to register bank 2
        BSF     3, 5        ;Go to register bank 3
        BCF     0x0C, 7     ;Allow EEPROM access
        BSF     0x0C, 0     ;Set the Read bit
        BCF     3,6         ;Return to register bank 2
        MOVF    0x0C, W     ;Move frequency to W register
        BCF     3,5         ;Return to register bank 0
```

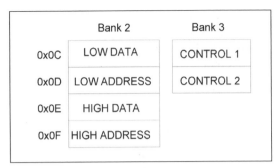

Fig 2.8: Registers used for Program Memory access

	Bank 2	Bank 3
0x0C	LOW DATA	CONTROL 1
0x0D	LOW ADDRESS	CONTROL 2
0x0E	HIGH DATA	
0x0F	HIGH ADDRESS	

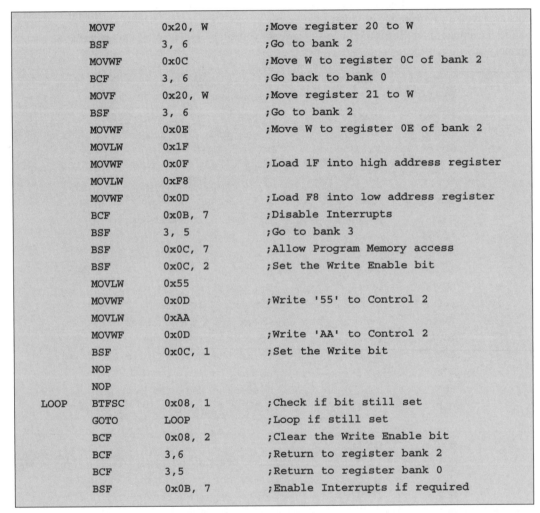

```
            MOVF     0x20, W      ;Move register 20 to W
            BSF      3, 6         ;Go to bank 2
            MOVWF    0x0C         ;Move W to register 0C of bank 2
            BCF      3, 6         ;Go back to bank 0
            MOVF     0x20, W      ;Move register 21 to W
            BSF      3, 6         ;Go to bank 2
            MOVWF    0x0E         ;Move W to register 0E of bank 2
            MOVLW    0x1F
            MOVWF    0x0F         ;Load 1F into high address register
            MOVLW    0xF8
            MOVWF    0x0D         ;Load F8 into low address register
            BCF      0x0B, 7      ;Disable Interrupts
            BSF      3, 5         ;Go to bank 3
            BSF      0x0C, 7      ;Allow Program Memory access
            BSF      0x0C, 2      ;Set the Write Enable bit
            MOVLW    0x55
            MOVWF    0x0D         ;Write '55' to Control 2
            MOVLW    0xAA
            MOVWF    0x0D         ;Write 'AA' to Control 2
            BSF      0x0C, 1      ;Set the Write bit
            NOP
            NOP
LOOP        BTFSC    0x08, 1      ;Check if bit still set
            GOTO     LOOP         ;Loop if still set
            BCF      0x08, 2      ;Clear the Write Enable bit
            BCF      3,6          ;Return to register bank 2
            BCF      3,5          ;Return to register bank 0
            BSF      0x0B, 7      ;Enable Interrupts if required
```

Listing 2.14: Writing to Program Memory

This allows numbers up to 16,383 to be stored whereas the maximum value that can be stored in a single EEPROM location is 255. In addition, any unused part of the program memory can be used for data. This is achieved by using two data and two address registers (**Fig 2.8**).

To write data into the program memory, both the high and low bytes of both the address and the data must be set. Then bit 7 of the Control 1 register must

```
BSF       3, 6            ;Go to bank 2

MOVLW     0x1F

MOVWF     0x0F            ;Load 1F into high address register

MOVLW     0xF8

MOVWF     0x0D            ;Load F8 into low address register

BSF       3, 5            ;Go from bank 2 to bank 3

BSF       0x0C, 7         ;Allow program Memory access

BSF       0x0C, 0         ;Set the Read bit

NOP

NOP

BCF       3, 5            ;Return to register bank 2

MOVF      0x0C, W         ;Move register 0C of bank 2 to W

BCF       3, 6            ;Go to bank 0

MOVWF     0x20            ;Move W to register 20 of bank 0

BSF       3, 6            ;Go back to bank 2

MOVF      0x0E, W         ;Move register 0E of bank 2 to W

BCF       3, 6            ;Go to bank 0

MOVWF     0x21            ;Move W to register 21 of bank 0
```

be set to a one, in order to tell the PIC to write data to the program memory rather than to EEPROM. However the greatest change concerns the timing.

Listing 2.15: Reading from Program Memory

When the PIC writes to program memory it totally suspends all other operations. This means that any counts and A/D conversions that are underway when the write happens are likely to give false answers. To ensure that the write does not create problems for the routine that is doing the write, at least two NOP instructions must be placed immediately after the instruction that sets the write bit.

For example, the code sample in **Listing 2.14** stores data in program memory address 1FF8 hex. It takes this data from registers 20 and 21 hexadecimal. (It

PIC programmer and experimentation board

27

```
MSG1      DATA         0x045, 0x054, 0x054, 0x04F, 0x054, 0x020
```

Listing 2.16: Declaring data in MPASM

```
          .MSFIRST
          .WORD        $044, $045, $053, $054
```

Listing 2.17: Declaring data in TASM

```
          BCF        3, 5
          BSF        3, 6             ;Go to bank 2
          MOVLW      0x07
          MOVWF      0x0F             ;Load 07 into high address register
          MOVLW      0xF0
          MOVWF      0x0D             ;Load F0 into low address register
NEXT      BSF        3, 5             ;Go from bank 2 to bank 3
          BSF        0x0C, 7          ;Allow program Memory access
          BSF        0x0C, 0          ;Set the Read bit
          NOP
          NOP
          BCF        3, 5             ;Return to register bank 2
          MOVF       0x0C, W          ;Move register 0C of bank 2 to W
          BTFSC      STATUS, ZERO     ;Check whether data is 0x00
          GOTO       DONE             ;Yes, so end
          BCF        3, 6             ;Go to bank 0
          MOVWF      PORTB            ;Write data to Port B
          CALL       WD               ;Write to display
          BSF        3, 6             ;Go to bank 2
          INCF       0x0D, F          ;Increment address to next character
          GOTO       NEXT             ;Get next character

DONE      BCF        3, 6             ;Go to bank 0
          MOVF       ERRNO, W         ;Get Error number
          CALL       XTABLE           ;Convert to ASCII
          MOVWF      PORTB
          CALL       WD
```

Listing 2.18: Data write routine

cannot take it from the W register as this is only 8 bits wide and the program memory can be 14 bits wide).

Reading the data from program memory requires that high and low byte addresses are specified to make up a full address. And two NOP instructions must be inserted after the read command. Finally, remember that the result could be up to 14 bits in length and this can not be accommodated in the eight bit W register.

The code sample in **Listing 2.15** reads data from program memory location 0x1FF8 and places it back into registers 20 and 21 hexadecimal.

```
ORG        0x07F0
DATA       " E r r o r  ", 0x00
```

The most useful application for the Program memory read facility is as a store for messages, such as error messages.

In this case, the data is loaded as part of the programming sequence. Note that each character is less than 8 bits in length. This means that it only uses two hexadecimal digits although this could be preceded by one or two zeros if required.

To declare the data when compiling the program with MPASM, use the command DATA. See, for example, **Listing 2.16**.

For TASM, use the .WORD command but this must be preceded by an .MSFIRST command, otherwise the characters are loaded incorrectly (**Listing 2.17**).

These commands can be used with text, such as DATA 'M e s s a g e' but each character must be preceded by a space. Otherwise, the compiler will try to pack two characters into a word and this will fail because each character requires 8 bits and there are only 14 available bits in each work. Preceding the characters with a space fills the upper 6 bits of each word with spaces and places the actual character in the lower 8 bits.

The code sample in **Listing 2.18** is called after placing the error number in a register called ERRNO. It reads the message from program memory location 0x07F0 and uses the standard technique of using the value of zero to indicate the end of the text part of the message. The routine outputs the message to an alphanumeric display that is connected to port B. It uses the subroutine 'WD' to manipulate the control signals that are required by the display and to add any necessary delays. The subroutine XTABLE is also used to convert binary codes to ASCII. The message is written as in **Listing 2.19**.

Listing 2.19: Declaring the data

Interrupts

Applications such as frequency counters and Morse generators are time critical so anything that interferes with the smooth running of these programs must be avoided. This type of program tends to allow more than enough time for peripherals, such as A/D converters, to finish before trying to read them and to ask port connected switches what state they are in at times when they need the information. However, there are other applications that don't need to do anything until something happens. For example, a PIC that provides frequency control for a transceiver does not need to do anything until the user changes frequency. Then it needs to update the frequency synthesiser and the display. Or, when the user changes the mode, it needs to update the modulator/detector and display.

Such applications can detect what the user is doing, by one of two ways:
- By asking (sometimes called polling) the keyboard and other peripherals
- By allowing the peripherals to interrupt whatever background task the PIC is doing.

Let me give an analogy to demonstrate how the two approaches work.
- Two companies sell equal amounts of goods per day and have an equal amount of customers when measured over a full day.
- Company A supplies its goods through mail order. The orders arrive at the start of the day and are placed in a pile. Workers take an order, pull the goods off the shelves and pack them. There is a bulk collection at the end of each day for delivery to their customers.

- Company B has a shop where customers come in to be served. However, they cannot predict with any accuracy when the customers will arrive. So sometimes the shop is empty. At other times, there are many customers in the shop. If customers have to wait too long, they leave without buying and the company loses business.
- In order to service the same number of customers, interrupt driven company B needs more staff than interrupt free company A. This is because they spend time doing nothing, apart from tidying the shop and making it look attractive, in order that there is enough staff to handle the busy periods. In addition, you can't ask a shop worker to do a job, such as stocktaking a section of the shop, without allowing them extra time to be interrupted by customers. With company A, there are no busy periods so staff can simply work steadily throughout the day. If you want a part of the warehouse to have a stock-take, you can simply schedule it as another job.

The same applies to interrupts. A program that uses interrupts must allow for the fact that it cannot predict exactly when they will occur. It must also ensure that any routine that is likely to be interrupted is not time critical.

With a PIC the default condition, that is the condition that will apply unless you do something, is that all interrupts are disabled. This means that the program will never be interrupted unless it needs to be. The only exception to this rule is the Watchdog timer, which must be enabled or disabled when the configuration word is written to the PIC.

In order to use interrupts, they must be enabled at both a global level and at an individual level. This approach allows all interrupts to be disabled temporarily, for example whilst undertaking a time critical part of a program, and then switch your selection of interrupts back on again by using a single instruction each time.

Interrupts can be generated by:

- The watchdog timer, although this is intended to be used in the detection of software bugs rather than as a true timer.
- Completion of writes to EEPROM
- Timers (Timer0, 1 or 2) overflowing. These can be selected individually.
- Port B Bit 0 pin changing to a selected state. Interrupts can be programmed to activate on either a positive-going or negative edge.
- Port B Bits 4 to 7 changing state. The interrupt occurs if any one (or more) of these pins changes state irrespective of how it changes. This interrupt is very useful for handling keyboards.
- Analogue to Digital (A/D) conversions completing.
- The communications channel receiving a character (byte).

Fig 2.9: Interrupt Registers

	Bit 7	6	5	4	3	2	1	0
INTCON	Global	PIE	Timer 0	Port B Bit 0	Port B Bits 4-7			
PIE 1		A/D	UART RX	UART TX	Sync Serial	Capture Compare	Timer 2	Timer 1
PIE 2				EEPROM write				Capture Compare2

- The communications channel being in a position to accept another character (byte) for transmission.

Interrupts are controlled by the INTCON register (register 0x0B in all register banks) and by the PIE (Peripheral Interrupt Enable) registers. These vary in number. For example, the 16F84 has no PIE registers but the 16F873 has two and these are located at 0x0C and 0x0D of register bank 2. **Fig 2.9** shows how this works.

(On PICs with no PIE registers, Bit 6 of the INTCON register is used for EEPROM write interrupts.)

To enable an interrupt, the appropriate bit must be set to a logic one. Individual bits should be enabled first. If these bits are within any of the PIE registers, the PIE bit of the INCON register (bit 6 of register 0x0B) must be enabled next. Finally, the global interrupt bit (bit 7 of the INTCON register) must be enabled.

As soon as the global interrupt is set, interrupts could occur and so the program must be ready for them. This means that the global interrupt bit must not be set until all the required registers have been initialised.

An interrupt is like a subroutine except that is has a fixed address in memory. When an interrupt occurs, the PIC completes the current instruction. It then stores the program counter, which points to the locations of the next instruction, in a way similar to the execution of a CALL instruction. The program counter is then loaded with the interrupt address, which is 0x04. At the end of the interrupt handling routine, the program executes a RETFIE instruction. This causes the PIC to recover the saved address and load it into the program counter. **Fig 2.10** illustrates this.

In practice, however, the main program is normally located at location 0x05 or 0x10. The instruction at location 0x04 then becomes a GOTO (or a disable interrupt followed by a GOTO) that jumps to the full interrupt handler, which is located after the main program in memory. This simply makes it easier to write the program.

If multiple interrupts have been enabled, the program must identify what has caused the interrupt - remembering that multiple interrupts may have occurred simultaneously. This is done by inspecting the INTCON and PIR registers. The PIR registers have the same register numbers as the PIE registers but they are in bank 1 rather than in bank 0 (**Fig 2.11**).

These bits are set to a logic one when the interrupt occurs. The interrupt handling routine must reset these bits. In the case of the timers, capture/compare and port B bits 4-7, this is done by removing the condition that caused the inter-

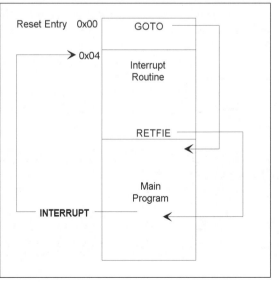

Fig 2.10: The operation of Interrupts

Fig 2.11: Interrupt sources

	Bit 7	6	5	4	3	2	1	0
INTCON						Timer 0	Port B Bit 0	Port B Bits 4-7
PIR 1		A/D	UART RX	UART TX	Sync Serial	Capture Compare	Timer 2	Timer 1
PIR 2				EEPROM write				Capture Compare2

rupt, such as emptying a timer. For the A/D, UART, Sync and EEPROM bits, these can be cleared directly in the INTCON and PIR registers.

Unless action is taken, there is nothing to stop the interrupt handler routine from being interrupted if another interrupt occurs. The PIC will handle this by remembering where it was in the interrupt handler when the new interrupt occurred. It can store up to six interrupt calls or subroutine calls. However, two problems can arise:

- The number of interrupts could exceed six. In this case, the PIC will simply forget the earlier addresses and routines may encounter return instructions with no address to return to. This will cause the program to crash and a reset or watchdog timer interrupt is likely to be the end result.

- The second interrupt handler is likely to clear both interrupts with the result that, on return the first interrupt, it has already been cleared. For example, if timer 1 causes an interrupt and the handler was just about to read it when a port B interrupt happened, a second call to memory location 0x04 will occur. When called, the handler does not know where the interrupt has come from. It therefore reads the condition that is being timed and resets it. It also handles the Port B interrupt and then returns to the point in the interrupt handler that it was at (just about to do a read) when the second interrupt occurred. However, the value that it reads is false because the second interrupt handler cleared it - but the interrupt handler doesn't know this so it works with this incorrect value.

Because of this, it is common practice to disable interrupts upon entry to the interrupt handler. The bits will still be set in the INTCON and PIR registers if the conditions for an interrupt occur, but there will be no call to address 0x04. When all of these bits are clear, interrupts are enabled again before a return from interrupt (RETFIE) is executed. Interrupts can be disabled or re-enabled with a single instruction (**Listing 2.20**).

Listing 2.20: Enabling and disabling Interrupts

The command BSF 0x0B, 7 will re-enable those interrupts that were enabled when interrupts were disabled unless changes have been made to the interrupt enable bits of the INTCON and PIE registers.

```
BCF       0x0B, 7        ;Disable Interrupts
GOTO INTERRUPT HANDLER

. . . . . .

. . . . . .

BSF       0x0B, 7        ;Enable Interrupts
RETFIE                   ;Return to calling routine
```

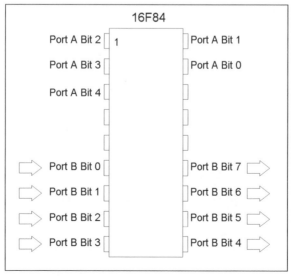

3

Peripherals

In the context of a PIC, the term 'peripheral' includes input/output ports, counters, converters and communications facilities. These facilities are built-into the chip although their capability will vary between chip types.

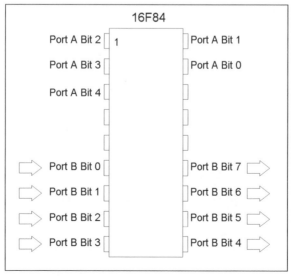

Fig 3.1: Bit settings

BIT	7	6	5	4	3	2	1	0
PORT B	0	0	0	0	1	1	1	1

Ports

All PIC chips have input/output ports although the exact number of ports, and the number of signals in each port, will vary between chip types.

It could also vary between applications because any analogue to digital (A/D) conversions, external counters or communications facilities will use signals that could otherwise be used as part of an input/output port.

Each pin of each port is individually configurable as input or output. This is done by going to register bank 1 and setting the appropriate bit to a one for an input or clearing it to a zero for an output. For example, to set port B so that bits 0 to 3 are outputs and bits 4 to 7 are inputs, move the value of 00001111 binary (0x0F hexadecimal) to register 6 in bank 1 (**Fig 3.1**).

If this is applied to a 16F84 chip, it will set pins 6 to 9 as inputs and pins 10 to 13 as outputs (**Fig 3.2**).

Fig 3.2: Signal directions

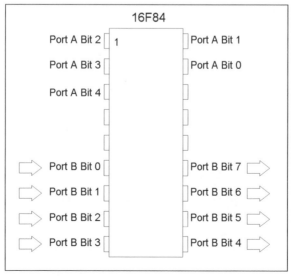

	BSF	3, 5	;Go to register bank 1
	MOVLW	0x0F	
	MOVWF	0x06	;Move the value 0x0F to Port B
	BCF	3, 5	;Go back to register bank 0

Listing 3.1: Setting port directions

The code to achieve this is shown in **Listing 3.1**:

Where bits do not exist, or are used for other purposes, they can be set to serve either as inputs or as outputs. An output or non-existent bit, or a bit that is used for other purposes, will always be read as a zero.

Some bits operate slightly differently to others and it is always worth consulting the data sheet if this is likely to make any difference to your application.

On input, ports C, D, E and port A bit 4 have a Schmitt Trigger, which requires signals of less than 0.2 volts for a logic zero and more than 4.2 volts for a logic one when the chip is operated from a 5 volt supply. The other pins use TTL inputs, which operate at +0.8 volts for a logic zero and +2.0 volts for a logic one.

On output, all pins use TTL levels (+0.1 volts for a logic zero and +4.7 volts for a logic one) except for bit 4 of port A, which is open collector with a maximum voltage of 8.5 volts.

Each output pin is capable of driving loads up to 20mA but this is subject to an overall maximum current for the chip, which is about 100mA for 18 pin chips and 200mA for 28 pin chips.

Note that, for 18 pin chips like the 16F84, this is less than eight times 20mA so the chip can not directly drive a seven segment display that requires 20mA per segment if all segments are lit.

Ports that are used as output registers can, in theory, be used to store data as well as to drive the pins. This means that you can read their value, modify them and output the new value. For example, the code in **Listing 3.2** counts down from 9 to 0 (in ASCII):

This routine relies on another subroutine, called DELAY, to provide a time delay. It also assumes that the port has been initialised for output and that no other signals are required to drive the display.

Listing 3.2: A count down routine

However, the read command actually reads the signal on the pins rather than what is in the register. This means that there are two potential problems with this approach.

	MOVLW	0x09	;Load with 9
LOOP	ADDLW	0x30	;Convert to ASCII
	MOVWF	PORT	;Output to port
	CALL	DELAY	;Wait for time (eg 1 sec)
	DECF	PORT, W	;Get current value from port
	ANDLW	0x0F	;Convert back to a number
	BTFSS	STATUS, ZERO	;Is it zero? (BTFSS 3, 2)
	GOTO	LOOP	;No, so continue
	ADDLW	0x30	;Yes, it's zero - convert to ASCII
	MOVWF	PORT	;Output to port
	RETURN		;Return to calling routine

1. If the port is a Schmitt trigger and the output has degraded to TTL levels, for example because the chip is providing very high currents, this may result in an incorrect reading.

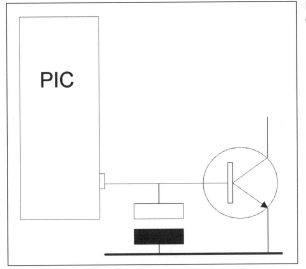

Fig 3.3: Capacitor on output

2. If the output is driving a capacitor then the pin may not yet have reached its final voltage (**Fig 3.3**).

In these circumstances, it may be better to keep the actual data in another register and copy the result to the port, as in **Listing 3.3**.

Counter/Timers

In addition to the Watchdog Timer, PICs can have up to three counter/timers. Each of these has slightly different capabilities:

- Timer 0 is an 8 bit timer that can be clocked from an external pin or the main PIC oscillator at a quarter of the main oscillator's speed. There is no explicit gate on the input to this timer but other ways of gating the input are discussed below. The prescaler for this timer is shared with the watchdog timer.
- Timer 1 is a 16 bit timer with a gated input. The input can be configured for a single ended signal or as a low frequency crystal oscillator. It has its own prescaler.
- Timer 2 is an 8 bit timer with an 8 bit comparator. It can only be clocked from the main PIC oscillator at a quarter of the main oscillator's speed. It has its own prescaler and a postscaler.

Listing 3.3: Using an intermediate register

```
        MOVLW   0x09            ;Load with 9
LOOP    ADDLW   0x30            ;Convert to ASCII
        MOVWF   REGX            ;Store in register
        MOVWF   PORT            ;Copy to port
        CALL    DELAY           ;Wait for time (eg 1 sec)
        DECF    REGX, W         ;Get current value from register
        ANDLW   0x0F            ;Convert back to a number
        BTFSS   STATUS, ZERO    ;Is it zero? (BTFSS 3, 2)
        GOTO    LOOP            ;No, so continue
        ADDLW   0x30            ;Yes, it's zero - convert to ASCII
        MOVWF   PORT            ;Copy to port
        RETURN                  ;Return to calling routine
```

Timer 0

The input can be switched to operate either from the PIC's internal clock which operates at one quarter of the oscillator

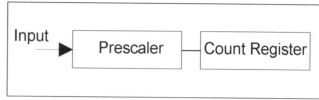

Fig 3.4: Timer 0 block diagram

speed, or from a pin that is shared with bit 4 of port A. This means that if you are using Timer 0 with an external input, you cannot use bit 4 of Port A as an output pin.

You could, however, still use it as an input pin if needed. Indeed, for this pin to act as an input to the timer, you must configure it as an input (BCF 5, 4) after moving to register bank 1 (BSF 3, 5)). The data source is selected by setting bit 5 of the option register (register 1 in bank 1). A logic one sets the input to port A bit 4 and a logic 0 to the internal clock. (See **Fig 3.4** for a block diagram).

It is also possible to specify whether the count changes on a positive-going or a negative-going edge. This is done by setting bit 4 of the option register (register 1 in bank 1).

A logic one increments the counter on a negative going edge and a logic zero on a positive going one.

The input goes into a prescaler. This is selectable to divide the input frequency by 1 (it passes through unaltered), or up to divide by 256 by changing bits 0 to 3 of the option register (register 1 of bank 1) as in **Table 3.1**.

If these bits are set to a code of 8 or more, the prescaler is assigned to the watchdog timer.

The count register is read as register 1 in bank 0 (or bank 3). Should the count overflow, (reaches a value of 256) it will set bit 2 of the INTCON

Bits	3	2	1	0		Division
0	0	0	0	(0)		2
0	0	0	1	(1)		4
0	0	1	0	(2)		8
0	0	1	1	(3)		16
0	1	0	0	(4)		32
0	1	0	1	(5)		64
0	1	1	0	(6)		128
0	1	1	1	(7)		256
1	0	0	0	(8)		1
1	0	0	1	(9)		1
1	0	1	0	(10 or 0x0A)		1
1	0	1	1	(11 or 0x0B)		1
1	1	0	0	(12 or 0x0C)		1
1	1	0	1	(13 or 0x0D)		1
1	1	1	0	(14 or 0x0E)		1
1	1	1	1	(15 or 0x0F)		1

Table 3.1: Prescaler settings

register (register 0x0B of any bank). If bit 5 of the INTCON register is set to a logic one, the overflow will cause an interrupt. This interrupt, and the bit 2 flag, are cleared by clearing the count register or setting it to a value of less than 256.

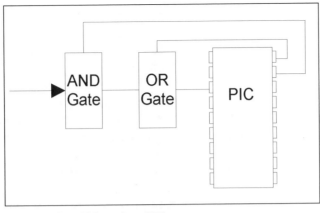

Fig 3.5: Using the prescaler as part of the counter

There are several issues that arise when trying to use Timer 0 in practical applications.

The first of these is that there is no input gate. The only way to stop the count is to keep clearing the count register or, if using an input from bit 4 or port A, by setting the pin to an output pin. However, you must make sure than any external circuitry can cope with the pin becoming an output.

The next issue regards its ablity to count precisely. For example, if you are trying to build an audio frequency counter that could measure up to 20kHz. The counter is only 8 bits and so it can count from zero to 255 and, if measuring Hz, this means that it could only count up to 255Hz.

To scale this up to 30,000, the prescaler should be set to 128. This means that the counter will now count up to 32767Hz (128*25) but only in 128Hz blocks. A frequency of 1kHz will register as 7, and 7 times 128 is 896. So the frequency is somewhere between 768 and 1023Hz. Some counters use a technique of adding extra pulses but this relies on having external gates. Take the circuit in **Fig 3.5** as an example:

The process operates as follows:
- The count register is cleared.
- The AND gate is opened (by setting bit 1 of port A to a logic one).
- The program waits for the required amount of time.
- The AND gate is closed (by setting bit 1 of port A to a logic zero).
- A copy of the count register is taken.
- Pulses are generated on bit 0 or port A. These go through the OR gate.
- Continue generating pulses until the count increases.
- Take another reading.
- Add one to the first count and multiply the whole number by the prescaler value
- Subtract the second count.

In this example, the first count would be 7 and the second count would be 24. Seven plus one is eight. Eight times 256 is 1024. 1024 minus 24 is 1000 and that is the frequency that we were measuring. The code sample in **Listing 3.4** demonstrates this approach.

The register TEMP is first used as part of the shift left code and then to hold the pulses. Changes in the count are detected by doing an exclusive OR

```
            CLRF        0x01               ;Clear Count Register
            BSF         PORTA, 1           ;Open Gate
            CALL        1SEC-DELAY         ;Allow 1 second delay
            BCF         PORTA, 1           ;Close Gate
            MOVF        0x01, W
            MOVWF       OLDCOUNT           ;Store copy of this count
            MOVWF       LOWCOUNT           ;Move Count to LowCount register
            CLRF        HICOUNT            ;Clear HighCount register
            BSF         3, 5               ;Go to register bank 1
            MOVF        0x01, W            ;Get Option Register
            ANDLW       0x07               ;Get Prescaler Value
            BCF         3, 5               ;Go back to register bank zero
            MOVWF       TEMP
LOOP        BCF         STATUS, CARRY      ;Clear carry bit
            RLF         LOWCOUNT, F        ;Multiple by 2 (and add carry)
            RLF         HICOUNT, F         ;Multiply by two and add carry
            DECFSZ      TEMP, F            ;Have we multiplied enough?
            GOTO        LOOP               ;No
            CLRF        TEMP               ;Yes (Redundant instruction
                                           ;added for clarity)
PULSE       BSF         PORTA, 0           ;Generate pulse
            BCF         PORTA, 0
            INCF        TEMP, F            ;Increment pulse count
            MOVF        0x01, W            ;Get new count
            XORWF       OLDCOUNT           ;Compare to old count
            BTFSC       STATUS, ZERO       ;Is it the same?
            GOTO        PULSE              ;Yes so add another pulse
            MOVF        TEMP, W            ;No so get number of pulses
            SUBWF       LOWCOUNT           ;Subtract from LowCount
            BTFSS       STATUS, CARRY      ;Is result less than zero
            DECF        HICOUNT, F         ;Yes so subtract one from HiCount
```

Listing 3.4: Incremental counting

between the current and previous counts. If they are the same, the result will be zero.

An alternative approach is to take two counts and to allow the counter to overflow in one of the counts. This removes the need for a gate or for adding extra pulses. Taking the example given above, of an audio frequency counter to measure up to 30kHz in 1Hz steps, the first count will be of exactly 1/128 seconds (7.8125ms). 1kHz will give a count of 7.

The count register is cleared and a second count, of exactly one second, is made. During this second, the register will count up to 256 and so overflow. It will do this seven times and finish with a count of 104. The first count is multiplied by the prescaler value and the second count is added so 7 times 128 is 896 and 896 plus 104 is 1000.

It should be noted that is not practicable to use interrupts to measure the number of times that the register overflows. This is because the only way to clear an interrupt from timer 0 is to write something to the register and, whatever is written to the register, it will disturb the count that is taking place.

Interrupts are useful if you need to count an exact number that is less that 256. For example, to set a condition where an interrupt occurs after 150 pulses, write the value of 106 into the count register and set the prescaler to divide by one. After an additional 150 pulses arrive, the counter will read 256 and thus overflow, causing an interrupt.

It is not possible to take an accurate count above 255 because it is not normally possible to know what the prescaler contains or to reset its contents to zero. For example, if the prescaler is set to divide by 256 and the count is set to 255, the count could overflow after another 256 pulses if the prescaler is clear. Alternatively, the count could overflow after just a single pulse if the prescaler contains 255.

The exception to this rule is where the count is continuous. For example, to produce a delay of 1 second (assuming that the PIC is being clocked from a 4MHz crystal). This clock means that the counter is clocked every 1µs (4MHz/4).

The prescaler is set to 16 and the delay starts when the timer overflows. To start the 1 second timer, clear the register called GATE (CLRF GATE) and enables timer 0 interrupts (bit 5 of register 0x0B in register bank 1). The code sample in **Listing 3.5** shows the interrupt handler.

Listing 3.5: A one second timer

```
INT     BTFSC    GATE, 0      Is timer already in progress
        GOTO     CONT1        ;Yes so go to continuation routine

        BSF      GATE, 0      ;No so start timer
        ******                Routine to start external goes here!
        MOVLW    0xF4
        MOVWF    TIMER        ;Load timer with value of 244
CLRET   CLRF     0x01         ;Clear Count Register
        RETFIE

CONT1   DECFSZ   TIMER, F     ;244 interrupts?
        GOTO     CLRET        ;No so clear count register & return
                              ;Yes so stop count
        BSF      0x03, 5      ;Go to register bank 1
        BCF      0x0B, 5      ;Stop Timer 1 interrupts
        BCF      0x03, 5      ;Go back to register bank 0
        NOP                   ;Use NOPs for delay
        MOVLW    0xBE
        MOVWF    TEMP         ;Software loop BE=190 (x 3 = 570)
DELAY1  DECFSZ   TEMP, F
        GOTO     DELAY1
        NOP
        ******                Routine to stop external goes here!
        RETFIE
```

Fig 3.6: Counter 1 block diagram

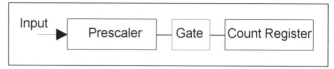

Input — Prescaler — Gate — Count Register

When the timer overflows, an interrupt occurs. Because the GATE register is clear, the timer is started. The TIMER register is loaded with 244 and the count register is cleared. It may appear that this is not necessary, as the count contains zero by virtue of the fact that it has just overflowed, but it is necessary to write to this register in order to clear the interrupt. Any external functions are also started.

The next time that an interrupt occurs will be exactly 4096µs later, because the prescaler is set to 16 and the clock is 1µs. Interrupts occur when the count register reaches 256 (256 times 16 is 4096). Bit 0 of the GATE1 register is now set so the routine goes to CONT1. This decrements the timer. If the timer is not zero, it clears the count register and continues. The count will reach zero after 244 interrupts at 4.096ms intervals, which is 999.424ms. At this point, the interrupt is disabled and a series of NOPS and a software loop is used to soak up the remaining 576µs.

Counter 1

At first sight, this counter (**Fig 3.6**) seems a lot more user-friendly than timer 0. It has:

- A 16 bit count register, so it will count up to 65,535.
- A gate so the count can be started and stopped under program control.
- An oscillator facility.

However, there are some issues that you need to be aware of:

- The prescaler is in front of the gate so it is not possible to know what value it contains when the gate is opened.
- The prescaler will only divide by 1, 2, 4 or 8.
- The count circuit will operate up to TTL speeds, but the oscillator facility has a maximum rated speed of 200kHz.
- The counter will only trigger on a positive going edge. Most of the other TTL based counters trigger on the negative going edge.

Like timer 0 this timer can take an input from the internal clock, at a quarter of the oscillator speed, or from an input pin (**Fig 3.7**). In this case the pin is shared with bit zero of port C. You also lose bit 1 of port C as this is used for the crystal oscillator (**Fig 3.8**).

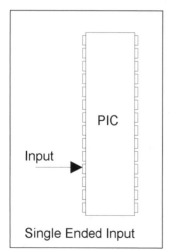

Single Ended Input

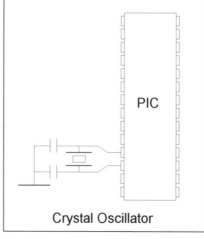

Crystal Oscillator

Fig 3.7: Single ended input

Fig 3.8: Crystal oscillator

```
CLRF        0x10              ;Stop Counter an clear prescaler
CLRF        0x0E              ;Clear low count
CLRF        0x0F              ;Clear high count
BSF         0x10, 1           ;External clock on bit 0 of port C
BSF         0x10, 0           ;Start Timer
CALL        Wait1Sec          ;1 second delay
BCF         0x10, 0
```

Bits	5	4		Division
0	0	(0)	1
0	1	(1)	2
1	0	(2)	4
1	1	(3)	8

Table 3.2: Prescaler control

Listing 3.6: Audio frequency counter

Timer 1 is controlled through register 0x10 of bank 0 - the T1CON register. This controls the timer gate (bit 0 - set to 1 to time/count an event), selects the clock source (bit 1 - 1 for external clock, 0 for internal clock), enables the oscillator (bit 3 - 1 for enabled).

The data is available through registers 0x0E for the low byte and 0x0F for the high byte. The code in **Listing 3.6** creates an audio frequency counter (capable of counting up to 65kHz). It assumes that bit 0 of port C has been set to an input pin.

If the frequency, that was being measured, was exactly 1000Hz then register 0x0F will contain the value of 3 and register 0x0E will contain the value of 0xE8 (E8 hexadecimal). 3E8 is the hexadecimal equivalent of 1000.

The prescaler is controlled by bits 4 and 5 of register 0x10 as shown in **Table 3.2**.

Timer 1 can also be configured to cause an interrupt on overflow. This is done by setting bit 0 of the Peripheral Interrupt Enable register (register 0x0C of register bank 1) to a logic one.

If an interrupt occurs, the flag bit (bit 0 of register 0x0C in register bank 0) will be set.

The code in **Listing 3.7** provides an interrupt every second. It is based on the use of a 32.768kHz crystal wired between bits 0 and 1 of port C.

The code in **Listing 3.8** loads the timer with the value of 0x8000. It will require exactly another 0x8000 pulses before it overflows. 0x8000 in hexadecimal is 32768 and this is the frequency of the crystal.

Listing 3.7: Interrupt handler

```
ORG         0x04
BCF         0x0B, 7           ;Disable Interrupts
MOVLW       0x80
MOVWF       0x0F              ;Set HiCount to 32768.
******                        Other routines go here
BSF         0x0B, 7           ;Enable Interrupts
RETFIE
```

```
BSF        3, 5              ;Go to register bank 1
BCF        PORTC, 0          ;Set Port C direction bits
BCF        PORTC, 1
BCF        3, 5              ;Go back to register bank 0
MOVLW      0x0A              ;Set Timer to external with no prescaler
MOVWF      0x10
CLRF       0x0E
MOVLW      0x80
MOVWF      0x0F              ;Load registers with 0x8000 (1 sec)
BSF        3, 5              ;Go to register bank 1
BSF        0x0C, 0           ;Set Interrupt enable
BCF        3, 5              ;Go back to register bank 0
BDF        0x0B, 6           ;Enable peripheral interrupts
BSF        0x0B, 7           ;Enable global interrupts
BSF        0x10, 0           ;Enable timer 1
```

Listing 3.8: Startup code

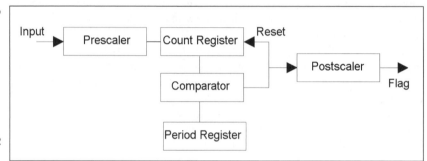

Fig 3.9: Counter 2 block diagram

Counter 2

Counter 2 (**Fig 3.9**) is an eight bit counter. It can only be driven from the internal clock. This goes through a prescaler and into the count register. When the count register is the same as the value in the period register, the count register is reset. So, if the internal clock is operating every 1μs, the prescaler is set to one and the period register is set to 250 (0xFA) then the count register will be reset every 250μs. Every time the count register is reset, a pulse is sent to the postscaler. Only when the postscaler overflows will the flag be set and an interrupt occur. So if the postscaler is set to 4, interrupts will be generated every 1ms.

Timer 2 is controlled by register 0x12 in register bank 0.

Bits 0 and 1 of register 0x12 control the prescaler (see **Table 3.3**).

Bit 2 turns the counter on and off. A logic one turns it on.

Bits 3 to 6 control the postscaler (see **Table 3.4**).

The period register is register 12 of bank 1 and it is possible to read the value in the count register by reading register 11 of register bank 0.

Bits	1	0	Division
0	0	(0)	1
0	1	(1)	4
1	0	(2)	16
1	1	(3)	16

Table 3.3: Counter 2 prescaler

Table 3.4: Counter 2 postscaler

Bits	6	5	4	3		Division
	0	0	0	0	(0)	1
	0	0	0	1	(8)	2
	0	0	1	0	(0x10)	3
	0	0	1	1	(x018)	4
	0	1	0	0	(0x20)	5
	0	1	0	1	(0x28)	6
	0	1	1	0	(0x30)	7
	0	1	1	1	(0x38)	8
	1	0	0	0	(0x40)	9
	1	0	0	1	(0x48)	10
	1	0	1	0	(0x50)	11
	1	0	1	1	(0x58)	12
	1	1	0	0	(0x60)	13
	1	1	0	1	(0x68)	14
	1	1	1	0	(0x70)	15
	1	1	1	1	(0x78)	16

Watchdog timer

All PIC chips have a watchdog timer. This uses a separate resistor/capacitor based oscillator that is sensitive to voltage and temperature. At 25°C (77°F) the time is about 18ms but this rises to about 23ms if the temperature rises to 100°C (212°F).

If the voltage drops to 3.3 volts (at 25°C) the time will be about 22ms and at 2.5 volts and 100°C the time will increase to about 38ms.

The watchdog timer can be prescaled but is shares a prescaler with timer 0. The prescaler is changed by changing bits 0 to 3 of the option register (register 1 of bank 1). See **Table 3.5**.

Bits	3	2	1	0		Division	Time
	0	0	0	0	(0)	1	18mS
	0	0	0	1	(1)	1	18mS
	0	0	1	0	(2)	1	18mS
	0	0	1	1	(3)	1	18mS
	0	1	0	0	(4)	1	18mS
	0	1	0	1	(5)	1	18mS
	0	1	1	0	(6)	1	18mS
	0	1	1	1	(7)	1	18mS
	1	0	0	0	(8)	1	18mS
	1	0	0	1	(9)	2	36mS
	1	0	1	0	(10 or 0x0A)	4	72mS
	1	0	1	1	(11 or 0x0B)	8	144mS
	1	1	0	0	(12 or 0x0C)	16	288mS
	1	1	0	1	(13 or 0x0D)	32	576mS
	1	1	1	0	(14 or 0x0E)	64	1.152 Secs
	1	1	1	1	(15 or 0x0F)	128	2.304 Secs

Table 3.5: Watchdog Prescaler

(Left) Fig 3.10: Setting the Watchdog timer in Progpic2

(Below) Fig 3.11: Setting the Watchdog with Send

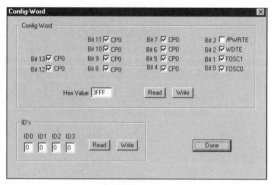

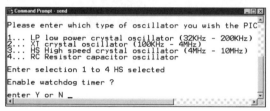

When the timer overflows, it will cause the PIC to be reset unless the PIC is in sleep mode. In this case it will simply wake up the program. To stop the watchdog timer from overflowing, execute CLRWDT instructions or disable the timer. The timer is enabled as part of the chip's configuration. This is done when the program is loaded into the PIC. Two methods of setting the watchdog timer are shown in **Figs 3.10 and 3.11**.

Analogue to digital converters

No PIC has more than one Analogue to Digital (A/D) converter but it is possible to switch the converter so that it converts analogue signals from different input pins.

Where the PIC has an A/D converter, it could either be an 8-bit convertor or a 10-bit converter. 10 bits converters can also be configured as 8 bit converters. If the converter is instructed to convert a voltage that is somewhere between zero and 5 volts, an 8-bit converter will give an accuracy of about 20mV whereas a 10-bit converter will be accurate to approximately 5mV. This means that if the input changes by less than that amount, the output may not change.

An A/D conversion works by comparing the incoming analogue signal against an internally generated Digital to Analogue (D/A) conversion in a series of successive approximations. **Fig 3.12** shows the block diagram.

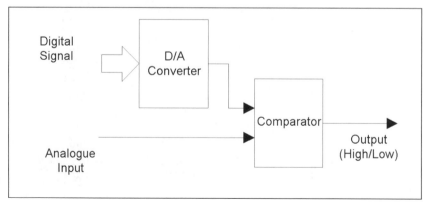

Fig 3.12: A/D block diagram

Test	Digital Signal	D/A	Comparator Output
1	10000000	2.5 volts	Low
2	01000000	1.25 volts	Low
3	00100000	0.625 volts	High
4	00110000	0.9375 volts	High
5	00111000	1.09375 volts	Low
6	00110100	1.015625 volts	Low
7	00110010	0.9765625 volts	High
8	00110011	0.99609375 volts	Low
9	00110011	0.99609375 volts.	

Table 3.6: A/D conversion process

For example, if the analogue signal is exactly 1 volt on a scale of zero to 5 volts, the calculations in **Table 3.6** take place.

Each test changes a bit in the digital signal to a one, starting with bit 7. If the comparator output is low, that bit is changed back to a zero as the next bit is being set to a one.

Each iteration of the D/A converter changes by half of the previous change so that the result, after 8 bits, is still 3.9mV away from the actual voltage. A 10 bit conversion would have continued for two more bits to give a result that is within 1mV of the original (0011001110).

All this takes time so it is not possible to get an instant result when you ask for a D/A conversion. The greater the number of bits in the conversion, the greater will be the conversion delay. In addition, there is a maximum frequency at which this circuit can operate and this is about 1.6μs.

The clock that drives the conversion process can be taken from an internal RC oscillator that runs at a speed of about 250kHz (4μS) or from a division of the main PIC oscillator. PICs that use 4MHz oscillators should take a division of 8, which gives an A/D conversion rate of 2μs, and those that run 20MHz clocks should use a division of 32 to give an A/D conversion rate of 1.6μs.

This time delay of 9 times the A/D conversion rate can either be calculated by the programmer or the program can monitor the state of the 'go' bit. This is set by the program to start a conversion and it is cleared by the PIC when the conversion finishes. Alternatively, the A/D converter can be programmed to generate an interrupt when a conversion is finished.

However, there is another timing issue with A/D conversions and this can only be handled by the programmer. The analogue input to the comparator must not change during the conversion process. To avoid this, the PIC uses a 'sample and hold' technique that is based on the use of a 'sample and hold' capacitor. However this capacitor needs time to charge. The exact time will depend on the amount of change on the signal and the impedance of the analogue circuit that is being sampled by the PIC.

Under normal circumstances (5 volt operation at 20-30°C) this charging time will be in the order of 8 to 16μs. What this means in practice is that when a sample is complete, the program should refrain from taking another sample for at least 16μs.

This in turn means that the maximum sampling rate is about 16000 samples per second.

Using the A/D converter therefore involves a number of steps:
- Selecting a reference voltage
- Changing the required pins to analogue
- Selecting the pin to convert
- If the converter is a 10 bit converter, deciding how to present the information
- Waiting for the input to settle
- Starting the conversion
- Waiting for the conversion to finish
- Reading the information

You can either choose the PIC's supply voltage to be the reference voltage or you can provide one. If you provide your own, it must not be more than the supply voltage to the PIC.

The reference voltage is the maximum voltage that the A/D can measure and the minimum voltage is zero.

The PIC cannot measure negative voltages. If the PIC is running in 8 bit mode, each step represents 1/256 of the reference voltage. For 10 bit conversions, each step is 1/1024.

The A/D converter is configured through register 0x1F in register banks 0 and 1. In bank 1, the register specifies which bits will be converted from digital to analogue use. In 10 bit counters, it also specifies how the 10 bits are to be split across two registers. A logic one in bit 7 of register 0x1F of register bank 1 indicates that the least significant 8 bits will be placed into register 0x1E of register bank 1 and the most significant two bits into register 0x1E of register bank 0.

In right justified conversion (**Fig 3.13**), a logic zero in bit 7 of register 0x1F of register bank 1 indicates that the most significant 8 bits will be placed into register 0x1E of register bank 0 and the most significant two bits into register 0x1E of register bank 1.

Bank 0								Bank 1							
0	0	0	0	0	0	Bit 9	Bit 8	Bit 7	Bit 6	Bit 5	Bit 4	Bit 3	Bit 2	Bit 1	Bit 0

Fig 3.13: Right justified conversion

Left justified conversion (**Fig 3.14**) is useful as it emulates an 8 bit converter, which places its results into register 0x1E of register bank 0.

The other bits in the configuration register 0x1F of register bank 1 identify which inputs of port A are changed from digital to analogue use:

Bank 0								Bank 1							
Bit 9	Bit 8	Bit 7	Bit 6	Bit 5	Bit 4	Bit 3	Bit 2	Bit 1	Bit 0	0	0	0	0	0	0

Fig 3.14: Left justified (8 bit emulation) conversion

Register 1F (Bank 1)			Port A pins					
Bit 2	Bit 1	Bit 0	Bit 0	Bit 1	Bit 2	Bit 3	Bit 4	Bit 5
0	0	0	Analogue	Analogue	Analogue	Analogue	Digital	Analogue
0	0	1	Analogue	Analogue	Analogue	Reference	Digital	Analogue
0	1	0	Analogue	Analogue	Analogue	Analogue	Digital	Analogue
0	1	1	Analogue	Analogue	Analogue	Reference	Digital	Analogue
1	0	0	Analogue	Analogue	Digital	Analogue	Digital	Digital
1	0	1	Analogue	Analogue	Digital	Reference	Digital	Digital
1	1	0	Digital	Digital	Digital	Digital	Digital	Digital
1	1	1	Digital	Digital	Digital	Digital	Digital	Digital

Table 3.7: Analogue and digital pin settings

This means that the minimum number of pins that can be converted for analogue use is three (Bits 0, 1 and 3) - see **Table 3.7**. Those pins that are identified as analogue pins should be configured in the port register as being for input. If an external reference is used, it should be connected to bit 3 of port A.

Register 0x1F of register bank 0 is used to switch the converter on, select the pin to be converted, select the conversion frequency and start the conversion process.

When setting A/D conversion control register (**Fig 3.15**), the GO bit (bit 2) should not be set at the same time as other bits.

Setting bit 0 to a logic one will switch the A/D converter on and reconfigure the selected pins from digital to analogue use. Bits 3, 4 and 5 will select the channel to be converted (**Table 3.8**).

Bits 6 and 7 select the clock speed that will be used for conversion (see **Table 3.9**).

Bit 7	6	5	4	3	2	1	0
Clock Select		Channel Select			GO		A/D on

Fig 3.15: A/D conversion control register

Bit 5	Bit 4	Bit 3	Pin
0	0	0	Port A Bit 0
0	0	1	Port A Bit 1
0	1	0	Port A Bit 2
0	1	1	Port A Bit 3 (if not being used as reference)
1	0	0	Port A Bit 5

Table 3.8: Input pin selection

Bit 7	Bit 6	Division	Max Clock Speed
0	0	Osc / 2	1.25MHz
0	1	Osc / 8	5 MHz
1	0	Osc / 32	20 MHz
1	1	Internal RC Osc	(500kHz)

Table 3.9: Conversion speeds

```
            BSF         3, 5                ;Go to register bank 1
            BSF         PORTA, 0            ;Change bit 0 of port A to input
            CLRF        PORTB               ;Set port B as output
            MOVLW       0x04                ;Select minimum number of Analog pins
            MOVWF       0x1F                ;and 8 bit emulation
            BCF         3, 5                ;Go back to register bank 0
            MOVLW       0x41                ;1/8 clock, Port A bit 0 & D/A on
            MOVWF       0x1F
            CALL        SETUPDELAY          ;16uS delay
            BSF         0x1F, 2             ;GO!
WAIT        BTFSC       0x1F, 2             ;Is Go bit still set
            GOTO        WAIT                ;No
            MOVF        0x1E                ;Yes so get result
            MOVWF       PORTB               ;Move to Port B
            RETURN
```

Listing 3.9: An A/D conversion routine

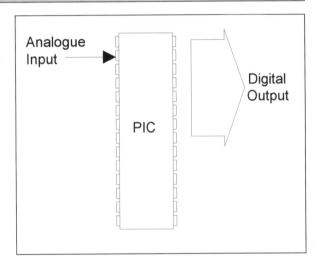

Figure 3.16: A/D conversion

The code in **Listing 3.9** will execute an 8 bit analogue to digital conversion (see **Fig 3.16**) on the signal arriving on Bit 0 of Port A, convert it to digital and output it on Port B.

It assumes that a 4MHz oscillator is being used and that the supply voltage will be used as the reference.

The BTFSC and GOTO sequence could be replaced by another delay (of more than 18ms) if this was more convenient.

As an alternative to waiting, an interrupt can be used. Set Bit 6 of the Peripheral Interrupt Enable register (register 0x0C in register bank 1). In addition, peripheral and global interrupts must be enabled (bits 6 and 7 of register 0x0B in any register bank) if these are not already set. When the interrupt occurs, it will set bit 6 of the Peripheral Interrupt Register (register 0x0C in register bank 0).

PIC to PC communications

This interface is based on the PC's 'COM' port interface. The COM port is sometimes also known as the V.24 or RS-232-C port. At first, the COM port was used for modems and serial printers, but with the rise of Universal Serial Bus (USB) devices the COM port is becoming less popular. However, most computers still have at least one 'COM' type serial communications port and even those that don't can use a converter unit from a USB port.

The COM port is a serial port. This means that the bits are sent down a single wire one after another. Each byte, or character, has its own synchronising system. A start bit precedes the character and a stop period follows each character. As long as the characters and their synchronising bits do not overlap, there is no restriction on the time between characters. It can vary from zero to hours, or even longer. In addition, because each character contains its own synchronisation, the speed of the two ends can vary by up to about 5% and the system will still work perfectly.

Baud rates

This ability to use slightly different speeds is important because the PIC's clock, for the COM function, is derived from the main oscillator and MHz crystals do not divide exactly into the normal speeds that COM ports use.

COM port speeds are normally measured in bits per second (normally called baud). The maximum throughput of a COM port in characters (or bytes) per second is a tenth of the baud rate. So a 9600 baud line will carry 960 characters per second.

The baud rate is set by writing a value into register 0x19 of register bank 1 according to the formula:

value = (osc/(64 x rate))-1 or value = (osc/(16 x rate))-1

depending on whether the baud rate switch (in register 0x18 of register bank 1) is set to low or high. **Table 3.10** shows the most common baud rates and the settings for the baud rate registers for a PIC using a 4MHz oscillator:

It should therefore be noted a higher crystal speed may be necessary for speeds of 38400 and above. **Table 3.11** shows the most common baud rates and the settings for the baud rate registers for a PIC using a 20MHz oscillator.

COM port Baud Rate	Actual Baud Rate	Error	PIC Oscillator	Register 0x19	High/Low
300	300	0.16%	4MHz	0xCF	Low (0)
600	601	0.16%	4MHz	0x67	Low (0)
1200	1202	0.16%	4MHz	0x33	Low (0)
2400	2404	0.16%	4MHz	0x19	Low (0)
4800	4808	0.16%	4MHz	0x0C	Low (0)
9600	9615	0.16%	4MHz	0x19	High (1)
19200	19231	0.16%	4MHz	0x0C	High (1)
38400	35714	6.99%	4MHz	0x06	High (1)
57600	62500	8.51%	4MHz	0x03	High (1)
115200	125000	8.51%	4MHz	0x01	High (1)

Table 3.10: Baud rates with a 4MHz crystal

49

COM port Baud Rate	Actual Baud Rate	Error	PIC Oscillator	Register 0x19	High/Low
1200	1221	1.73%	20MHz	0xFF	Low (0)
2400	2404	0.16%	20MHz	0x81	Low (0)
4800	4808	0.16%	20MHz	0x40	Low (0)
9600	9615	0.16%	20MHz	0x81	High (1)
19200	19231	0.16%	20MHz	0x40	High (1)
38400	37878	1.36%	20MHz	0x20	High (1)
57600	57818	1.36%	20MHz	0x15	High (1)
115200	113636	1.36%	20MHz	0x0A	High (1)

For the most accurate baud rate, at speeds of 1200bps and above, a 14.7456MHz crystal is best (see **Table 3.12**). These can currently be obtained at reasonable prices from a number of sources. However, this speed may not be acceptable for other parts of the application and so a compromise may be necessary.

COM port Baud Rate	Actual Baud Rate	Error	PIC Oscillator	Register 0x19	High/Low
1200	1202	0.00%	20MHz	0xBF	Low (0)
2400	2404	0.00%	20MHz	0x5F	Low (0)
4800	4808	0.00%	20MHz	0x2F	Low (0)
9600	9615	0.00%	20MHz	0x17	Low (0)
19200	19231	0.00%	20MHz	0x0B	Low (0)
38400	35714	0.00%	20MHz	0x05	Low (0)
57600	62500	0.00%	20MHz	0x03	Low (0)
115200	125000	0.00%	20MHz	0x01	Low (0)

Table 3.12: Baud rates with a 14.7456MHz crystal

All of these figures for a 14.7456MHz crystal are given with bit 2 register 0x18 (in register bank 1) set to a zero for low baud rates. To change this so that the high baud rate setting can be used, add one to the value then divide by four. Finally, subtract one from the total to give the new value. There is no advantage in using high or low bit rates if the timing is accurate.

A 3.6864MHz crystal is also an exact match and it can be used at speeds down to 300bps but I have not found these available at reasonable prices. Of course, there are many companies that will manufacture any frequency to order but they naturally charge a premium for these.

Voltages

The PIC's COM function, which is also known as a Universal Synchronous/Asynchronous Receiver/Transmitter (USART), uses bit 6 and 7 of port C. These bits must both be set as input bits on the port even though bit 6 is used to transmit data. In addition, the USART must be enabled by setting bit 7 of register 18 in register bank 0.

It should be noted that the PIC generates signals of +5 volts for a logic one and zero volts for a logic zero. The official RS-232-C specification for the COM

Bit 7	6	5	4	3	2	1	0
Not used	Send 9 bits	TX enable	Must be 0	Not used	Speed High/Low	TX Buffer Empty	9th data bit

port states that a negative voltage should be used for a logic one and a positive voltage should be used for a logic zero. These voltages should be in the range of 6 to 15 volts. There are various ways of obtaining these voltages. Some applications have both positive and negative voltages available. Others derive it from the interface. I tend to use the Maxim MAX202 (or MAX232) chips as these have built in voltage converters and run from a single 5 volt line.

Table 3.13: TXSTATUS Register

USART transmitter

Once the pins have been converted for USART use, the PIC can send a character (or byte) to the computer by putting the character into register 0x19 of register bank 0, after setting the baud rate, switching on the transmitter and setting the transmit parameters. These parameters are set in the transmitter status (TXSTATUS) register, which is register 18 of register bank 1 (**Table 3.13**).

Although the PIC supports 9 bit transmissions, most PCs can only use the 9th bit for parity. Parity is an error detection mechanism. The PIC will only support parity if the program calculates and checks it for errors.

Bit 1 of register 18 in register bank 1 can be monitored to identify when the PIC is ready for the next character, but there is another way and that is to use bit 4 of register 0x0C in register bank 0. This avoids the need to change register banks.

The code in **Listing 3.10** (overleaf) is based on a PIC with a 20MHz crystal. It will set the baud rate to 19200bps, then it will start the transmitter and then send continuously to the PC the characters 'P', 'I' 'C' and a space. This is done without parity. The result is shown in **Fig 3.17**.

Note that after each character has been moved into the transmit data register (register 0x19 of register bank 0), a NOP is sent before bit 4 of the Peripheral Interrupt Register (register 0x0C of register bank 0) is monitored. Although this is not mentioned in Microchip's literature, it has been found necessary to insert an extra instruction at this point for correct operation.

An alternative is to use interrupts. These are enabled by setting bit 4 of the Peripheral Interrupt Enable register (register 0x0C of register bank 1). However, it should be noted that these techniques are only necessary if characters are being sent at or close to the line speed.

An alternative approach may be to increase the line speed and to leave gaps between characters. That way, the transmit buffer will empty quicker and there will be less danger of characters overlapping. At 1200 baud, a character will take 8.3ms to send whereas at 38400 baud each character takes only 260.1µs.

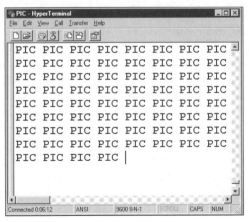

Fig 3.17: HyperTerminal display

```
            BSF      0x03, 5          ;Go to register bank 1
            MOVLW    0xC0
            MOVWF    PORTC            ;PORTC = Output except UART
            MOVLW    0x41             ;Set Baud rate to 19200
            MOVWF    0x19
            BCF      0x18, 4          ;Switch to COM port mode
            BCF      0x18, 6          ;Ensure 8 bit operation
            BSF      0x18, 2          ;Switch Baud Rate generator to High
            BSF      0x18, 5          ;Switch TX circuits on
            BCF      0x03, 5          ;Go back to register bank 0
            BSF      0x18, 7

START       MOVLW    0x50             ;Letter P
            MOVWF    0x19             ;Move to TX register
            NOP
WAIT1       BTFSS    0x0C, 4          ;Is TX register empty?
            GOTO     WAIT1            ;No so wait
            MOVLW    0x49             ;Letter I
            MOVWF    0x19             ;Move to TX register
            NOP
WAIT2       BTFSS    0x0C, 4          ;Is TX register empty?
            GOTO     WAIT2            ;No so wait
            MOVLW    0x43             ;Letter C
            MOVWF    0x19             ;Move to TX register
            NOP
WAIT3       BTFSS    0x0C, 4          ;Is TX register empty?
            GOTO     WAIT3            ;No so wait
            MOVLW    0x20             ;Space
            MOVWF    0x19             ;Move to TX register
            NOP
WAIT4       BTFSS    0x0C, 4          ;Is TX register empty?
            GOTO     WAIT4            ;No so wait
            GOTO     START
```

Listing 3.10: UART transmit

USART receiver

The receiver can hold two characters and be in the process of receiving a third without overflowing, so there is no need to empty the receiver's data register every time that it fills. However, as soon as the receiver has one full character that is available for transfer to another part of the PIC, it will set bit 5 of the Peripheral Interrupt Register (register 0x0C of register bank 0). It will also generate an interrupt if bit 5 of the Peripheral Interrupt Enable register (register 0x0C of register bank 1) is set.

To use the USART receiver, both bits 6 and 7 of Port C must be set as inputs and bit 4 of the TXSTATUS register (register 18 of register bank 1) must be cleared to a zero. Other aspects of the receiver are set through the RXSTATUS register, which is register 18 of register bank 0.

Bit 7	6	5	4	3	2	1	0
USART enable	Receive 9 bits	Not used	RX enable	Not used	Framing Error	Overrun Error	9th data bit

Both bits 7 and 4 of the RXSTATUS register (**Table 3.14**) must be set to a logic one for the receiver to operate. (Bit 7 must also be set for the transmitter to operate). Bit 6 is only set if the computer is sending 9 bit characters or 8 bits plus parity. Note that, if parity is being used, your program must provide any checking that is required.

Table 3.14: RX-STATUS Register

Characters are read from register 0x1A of register bank 0, unless they are 9 bits in length. In this case, register 0x1A of register bank 0 provides the lower 8 bits whilst the most significant (or parity) bit is placed in bit 0 of register 0x18 of register bank 0.

Bits 1 and 2 of the RXSTATUS register provide limited error checking. If bit 2 is set, it indicates that there has been an error in the format of the last character. This bit is automatically reset when a correctly formatted character is received. It should be noted that if a character is corrupted too far, this bit might not be set.

Bit 1 indicates that the three character buffer has overrun and that data has been lost. If this bit is set then no further characters will be received until bit 4 of the RXSTATUS register is cleared to a zero and then set back to a logic one again. This stops the USART receiver and then re-enables it.

The code segment in **Listing 3.11** reads characters from the USART and sends them to an alphanumeric display that is connected to port B. No error

Listing 3.11: UART receive

```
          BSF      0x03, 5       ;Go to register bank 1
          MOVLW    0xC0
          MOVWF    PORTC         ;PORTC = Output except UART
          CLRF     PORTB         ;PORTB = All outputs
          MOVLW    0x41          ;Set Baud rate to 19200
          MOVWF    0x19
          BCF      0x18, 4       ;Switch to COM port mode
          BSF      0x18, 2       ;Switch Baud Rate generator to High
          BCF      0x03, 5       ;Go back to register bank 0
          BSF      0x18, 7       ;Switch USART on
          BSF      0x18, 5       ;Switch receiver on
          BCF      0x18, 6       ;Ensure 8 bit operation


START     BTFSS    0x0C, 5       ;Any characters in USART RX?
          GOTO     START         ;No so wait

          MOVF     0x1A, W       ;Yes so move character to W
          MOVWF    PORTB         ;Move to Port B
          CALL     WD            ;Strobe and wait for display
          GOTO     START
```

checking is provided. The subroutine 'WD' is used to manipulate the control signals that are required by the display and to add any necessary delays. Note that the speed of the alphanumeric display may limit the maximum data transfer rate from the computer.

The USART also supports 'Synchronous Mode' operation. With this mode, one end is configured for master and the other for slave. Data is sent via bit 7 and a clock is sent via bit 6 of port C. This means that synchronous mode is an alternative to the COM port type mode that is described above. With Synchronous mode communications, only one end can transmit at any time and the other end must be in receive mode. Data is sent as a block with each block either being of a known size or an agreed terminating character used. Note that synchronous mode is not compatible with the AX-25 Amateur Radio mode protocol.

It should also be noted that the PIC does not directly support the five bit BAUDOT code that is used in radio teletype.

4

Programming for external circuits

E very instruction that the PIC executes takes time. Nothing happens in a PIC program instantly. Most instructions take one instruction cycle time, which is four oscillator pulses. This means that if the oscillator is running at 4MHz, the instruction cycle time is 1MHz or 1μs. A 20MHz oscillator has a 5MHz (or 200ns) instruction cycle time. However, the following instructions take two instruction cycle times:

- GOTO
- CALL
- RETURN, RETFIE (Return from Interrupt) and RETLW (Return with Literal in 'W')
- INCFSZ and DECFSZ but only if the result is zero and the next instruction is skipped. If the result is not zero, and the next instruction is executed, the instruction takes only one instruction cycle time.
- BTFSS and BTFSC but only if the condition is true and the next instruction is skipped. If the condition is not true, and the next instruction is executed, the instruction takes only one instruction cycle time.

Take, for example, the code fragment in **Listing 4.1**. The PIC will execute the code in the time stated in **Table 4.1**.

Listing 4.1: Short timing loop

```
        MOVLW    0x03           ;Load register TEMP with the value of 3
        MOVWF    TEMP
LOOP    DECFSZ   TEMP, F        ;Decrement TEMP and check if zero
        GOTO     LOOP           ;Not zero so go back to decrement
again
        NOP                     ;End of loop
```

Instruction		Time (cycles)	Time (total)	Content of TEMP
MOVLW	0x03	1	1	?
MOVWF	TEMP	1	2	3
DECFSZ	TEMP, F	1	3	2
GOTO	LOOP	2	5	2
DECFSZ	TEMP, F	1	6	1
GOTO	LOOP	2	8	1
DECFSZ	TEMP, F	2	10	0
NOP		1	11	0

Table 4.1: Timings for the short loop

Note that the DECFSZ is executed three times, because the register is loaded with the value of 3. And when the DECFSZ results in TEMP having a content other than zero, the time is 1 cycle. However, a GOTO is then executed and a GOTO is a 2 cycle instruction. This means that each loop takes 3 cycle times. Where the content of TEMP is zero, the DECFSZ time is 2 cycles but a single cycle instruction is then executed meaning that this is also a 3 cycle loop. So the total time is directly related to the number that is loaded into the register. It is (N times 3) plus 2 where N is the number that is loaded into the register. So, a value of 3 will take 11 cycles. A value of 100 (decimal - 0x64 hexadecimal) will take 302 cycles. The maximum value is where the register is cleared. The first DECFSZ, which should really be described as "decrement F and then skip if the result is zero", will first subtract one from this number. The result will therefore be 255. As this is not zero, the next instruction will be executed. As the clear can be executed in a single 'CLRF TEMP' instruction rather than two (MOVLW and then MOVWF), the formula becomes (N times 3) plus 1 and this loop will take (256 times 3) plus 1, or 769 cycles.

769 cycles on a PIC with a 4MHz oscillator will take 769µs but a PIC with a 20MHz crystal will execute the same routine in 153.8µs. This time can be extended in a number of ways:

- By executing multiple loops, one after another
- By extending the number of instructions in each loop, for example by using NOP instructions that take 1 instruction cycle each to execute. For example **Listing 4.2**:
- This example has three extra NOP instructions in each loop to the formula becomes (N times 6) plus 2 cycle times.
- By nesting loops as shown in **Listing 4.3**:

This example uses two nested loops. TEMP1 is loaded with 3 and TEMP2 with 100 decimal (0x64 hexadecimal). The inner loop (LOOP2) decrements TEMP2 until it is empty. This takes (100 times 3) plus 2 or 302 cycles. When TEMP2 becomes empty, TEMP1 is decremented. Then, TEMP2 is loaded with 100 once again. So the program will go round this outer loop three times. Therefore the overall time is ((TEMP2 times 3) plus (2 plus 3) times (TEMP1 plus 2) - or 917 cycles. The inner loop takes (TEMP2 times 3) plus 2 cycles. The 2 extra cycles are the MOVLW 0x64 and the MOVWF. The 3 cycles are a DECFSZ and a GOTO or a DECFSZ and a NOP. When this inner loop finishes, another DECFSZ and a GOTO (or a DECFSZ and a NOP) are executed so this accounts for the 'plus 3'. This outer loop is executed three times, as this is the value that is loaded into TEMP1. The final 'plus 2' is the initial MOVLW 0x03 and the MOVWF.

Listing 4.2: Extending loop times

```
        MOVLW   0x03            ;Load register TEMP with the value of 3
        MOVWF   TEMP
LOOP    NOP
        NOP
        NOP
        DECFSZ  TEMP, F         ;Decrement TEMP and check if zero
        GOTO    LOOP            ;Not zero so go back to decrement again
        NOP                     ;End of loop
```

56

```
          MOVLW    0x03                ;Load TEMP1 with 3
          MOVWF    TEMP1
LOOP1     MOVLW    0x64                ;Load TEMP2 with 100 (decimal)
          MOVWF    TEMP2
LOOP2     DECFSZ   TEMP2, F            ;Decrement TEMP2 and check if zero
          GOTO     LOOP2               ;Not zero so go back to decrement
again
          NOP                          ;Zero, so continue
          DECFSZ   TEMP1, F            ;Decrement TEMP1 and check if zero
          GOTO     LOOP1               ;Not zero so reload TEMP2
          NOP                          ;End of loop
```

I know that this seems complex but it provides an extremely accurate way of **Listing 4.3: Nested** using time. It can be trimmed to very accurate levels by adding NOP instruc- **loops** tions as these take up a single instruction cycle time.

When working with timing loops, programmers need to decide:
- What the loop period should be
- What must be done inside the loop and what can be done outside of it
- How accurate the loop period must be.

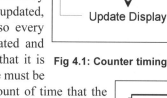

For example, a frequency counter that is accurate to 1kHz needs to open a gate for exactly 1ms and then close it again (**Fig 4.1**). This exact time can be calculated by executing a loop, possibly with a few NOPs for final trimming. If the frequency counter is using a seven segment LED display, this needs to be updated every 1 - 2ms and this could take a variable amount of time so this can be updated outside of the loop.

However, if the counter is switched so that it is accurate to 1Hz then the gate must be kept open for exactly one second. As the display still needs to be updated, this has to be done inside the timing loop so every instruction of the update needs to be calculated and every alternative path has to be trimmed so that it is **Fig 4.1: Counter timing** exactly the same length. Then, this update time must be subtracted from the gate time to find the amount of time that the loop must use.

Switches

Just about all radio systems use switches. Whether it is an on/off (toggle) switch, a push button or a rotary switch, switches are an excellent way for the user to make a choice. A synthesised rig, for example, could have a rotary switch (or encoder) to select the frequency. It could also have up/down switches or even a keyboard to type in the exact frequency required.

The simplest way to interface a switch to a PIC is simply to wire it between one of the pins on port B and zero volts (**Fig 4.2**).

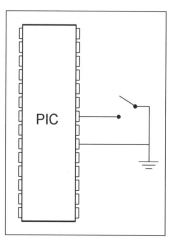

Fig 4.2: Simple switch connection to Port B

Then switch on the PIC's internal pull-up circuit so that the line is pulled up to a logic one when the switch is open. The pull-up circuit is enabled by clearing bit 7 of the OPTION register (register 1 in register bank 1). However, it should be noted that the pull-up applies only to port B, can only be enabled or disabled for every bit in port B and is equivalent to having a resistor of about 20kΩ (The specification says 12kΩ-100kΩ). For any other port, or if some bits can't have the internal pull-ups, you will have to provide your own. I tend to use a value of about 10kΩ.

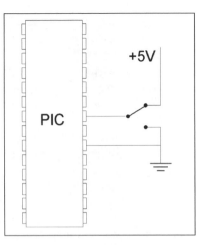

Fig 4.3: Two way switch can be connected to any port

Programming these simple switches can be done by using bit test instructions. The bit will be set if the switch is open and cleared if the switch is closed. Of course the port bit must be initialised as an input.

An alternative is to switch the pin between zero and 5 volts by using a two-way switch (**Fig 4.3**).

Using these approaches, the maximum number of switches is limited by the number of port bits that can be spared for this purpose. However, by wiring the switches to form a matrix, the number of switches can be increased (**Fig 4.4**). For example, the following diagram shows the 8 bits of port B linked to a 4 by 4 switch matrix, giving 16 switches in all and using just 8 lines.

Adding a 3 bit to 8 line decoder, such as a 74LS138, extends the number of switches to 32 using only 7 port interface bits (**Fig 4.5**). A 4 bit to 16 line decoder would allow 32 switches on just 8 port interface bits.

Programming a matrix of switches is a little bit more complex than a simple switch. Let me use **Fig 4.5** as an example. Firstly, the port needs to be initialised so that bits 4 to 6 of port B are outputs and the other bits are inputs. The pull-ups should also be enabled. Then, place a code of zero on the output pins and

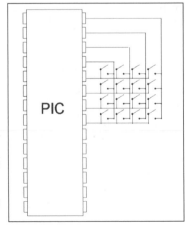

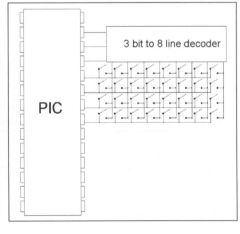

(left) Fig 4.4: 16 switch matrix

(right) Fig 4.5: 32 switch matrix

read the inputs. The decoder will place a zero volt signal on the left hand output line and this goes to the four switches on the left hand side. If these switches are open, the pull-ups will ensure that all inputs are at a logic one but a closed switch will take the line down to a logic zero. Once these four switches have been handled, the output bits are changed to '001'. The decoder then moves on to the next four switches and this can continue until all of the switches have been handled.

To find out if a switch has changed, it can be exclusive-'OR'ed against the state that it was in the last time that it was looked at. If any of the switches have changed state, this will be result in a logic change in the appropriate position.

The code fragments in **Listings 4.4 and 4.5** demonstrate this. Switches are numbered 0x01, 0x02, 0x04, 0x08, 0x11, 0x12 and so on up to 0x74 and 0x78. Registers 0x20 to 0x27 are used to hold the current switch states, and a register called COUNT is used as a count for the decoder. One other register is needed and this is called TEMP. It is used to build up the switch number, The subroutine SWITCH is called to handle the change when a press-key switch changes state, even if it has been released. The switch number is in the W register.

Port B and the registers are initialised. The eight comparison registers must have consecutive register numbers but COUNT and TEMP can be anywhere. In the main loop, a count of 0 to 7 is established with the number being incremented each time the loop goes around. To avoid the count going beyond 7 it is ANDed with 0x07. The count is used for two purposes:

1. To feed the decoder so that the decoder places a logic zero on the appropriate column of switches
2. After adding hex 20 it is placed in the FSR register. When this happens, register 0x00 (INDR) becomes synonymous with the register whose number is in the FSR register. So if the FSR register contains 0x24, register 0x00 is the same as register 0x24.

The decoder bits are obtained by swapping digits on the count and sending it to port B. This means that if the count is 0x04, a value of 0x40 is sent to port B. A short delay is then executed. This allows time for voltages to settle before port B is read. Then, after removing any extraneous bits, the data is compared with

Listing 4.4: Initial-isation code

BSF	3, 5		;Go to register bank 1
MOVLW	0x0F		
MOVWF	PORTB		;Port B bits 0-3 input, 4-7 output
BCF	3, 5		;Go back to register bank 0
MOVWF	0x20		;Write 0x0F to registers 20-27
MOVWF	0x21		
MOVWF	0x22		
MOVWF	0x23		
MOVWF	0x24		
MOVWF	0x25		
MOVWF	0x26		
MOVWF	0x27		
CLRF	COUNT		;Clear Decoder Address count

```
LOOP     INCF      COUNT, W        ;Increment to next decoder row
         ANDLW     0x07            ;Ensure that it doesn't go too far
         MOVWF     COUNT           ;Write back to Decoder Address
         ADDLW     0x20            ;Add 20 to give 20-27 hex
         MOVWF     0x04            ;Write to FSR
         SWAPF     COUNT, W        ;Move decoder address (01 becomes 10)
         MOVWF     PORTB           ;Output to Port B
         NOP                       ;Delay for voltages to settle
         NOP
         MOVF      PORTB, W        ;Read Port B
         ANDLW     0x0F            ;Weed out inputs
         XORWF     0x00, W         ;Exclusive OR with register 20-27 hex
         BTFSC     STATUS, ZERO    ;Is result zero?
         GOTO      LOOP            ;Yes so no switches changed
         MOVWF     TEMP            ;No - switches changed so store result
         MOVF      PORTB, W        ;Get switch states again
         ANDLW     0x0F            ;Weed out inputs
         MOVWF     0x00            ;Update register 20-27 hex
         SWAPF     COUNT, W        ;Get decoder row number
         ADDWF     TEMP, W         ;Add switch number
         CALL      SWITCH          ;Call switch handling subroutine
         GOTO      LOOP            ;Go to next decoder column.
```

Listing 4.5: Main code fragment
a previous scan of the same column. (Column 0 is kept in register 0x20, column 1 in 0x21 and so on, to column 7 being in register 0x27). If the switches are the same as the last scan, the loop continues with the column number being incremented but, if a switch is changed, the subroutine SWITCH is called. But first, the switch number is built up from the changes detected by the exclusive OR and the column number. In addition Port B is rescanned and the new scan is written back into the appropriate register in the range of 0x20 to 0x27.

If there is any danger that multiple switches will be closed at the same time,

Fig 4.6: False response

it may be necessary to place diodes in series with the switches. Otherwise, false results may occur as signals pass through multiple switches and give the appearance of additional switches being closed. **Fig 4.6** demonstrates this effect. It appears that switch 04 is closed even though it is open because the signal passes through switches 01, 21 and 24, which are all closed.

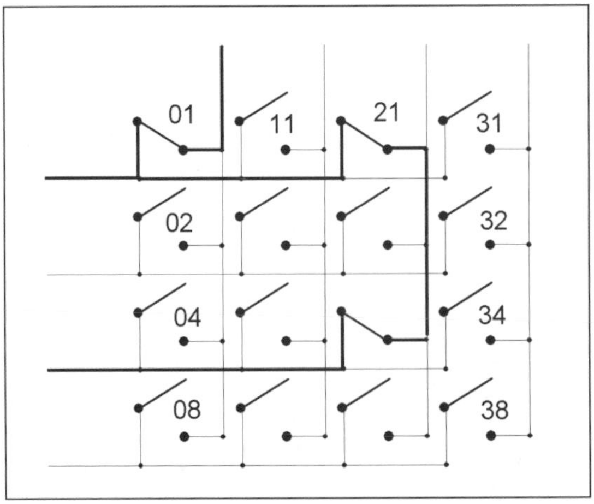

60

Lights

The simplest of all output devices is a light and the simplest of all lights to use is probably the Light Emitting Diode (LED). LEDs can be obtained in a variety of colours, size and brightness. Simply configure the appropriate bit on the port for output and connect the LED to it (**Fig 4.7**).

If the LED is not a 5 volt type, connect a resistor in series with it. Adjust the value for an appropriate brightness, but not less than 180Ω is a good general rule. Make sure that the LED is the correct way round.

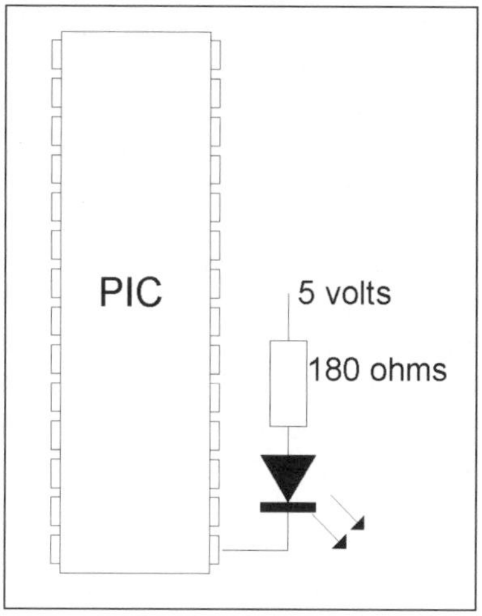

Fig 4.7: LED connected to a port

Some people wire their LEDs from the pin to ground but I prefer to wire mine between the pin and the +5 volt line. That way, there is no danger that it will suffer interference from any internal pull-up resistors, should the port be switched to input mode.

With the LED wired in this way, up to the +5 volt line, the bit must be cleared to a logic zero for the light to come on and set to a logic one for the light to be extinguished.

As with switches, more lights can be accommodated by using a matrix that is either driven directly from other port bits or driven via a decoder such as the 74LS138 (or 74HC138 or 74HCT138).

A 74LS138 and four other port bits will drive up to 32 LEDs (**Fig 4.8**). The LEDs cannot all be switched on at the same time but this doesn't matter.

As long as a LED is switched on at least 20 times a second and remains on for at least 10% of the time it will appear to have been switched on continuously.

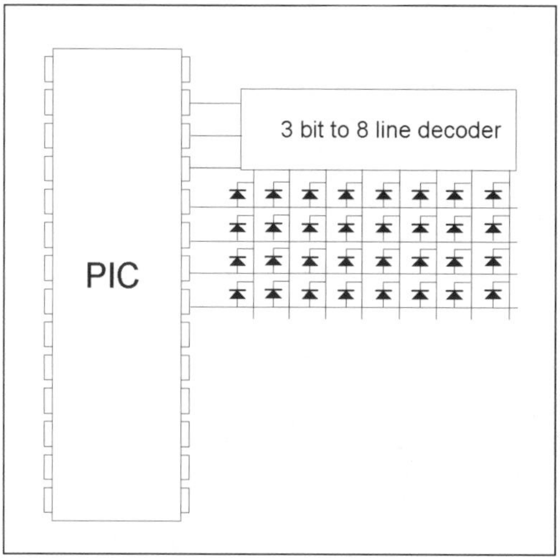

This effect, which is known as the persistence of vision, is the principle behind cinema and television where a series of still pictures is seen as a continuously moving image.

One problem with this approach is that the PIC and the 74LS138 can each handle only 20-25mA per pin.

With a large number of LEDs that could potentially be on at the same time, the options are to use low current LEDs or to boost the current with an additional transistor as

Fig 4.8: Multiplexed LEDs

shown in the diagram, **Fig 4.9**. (Only one output of the 74LS138 is shown for clarity).

PNP transistors, such as 2N2907 or 2N3906, are used in this application because the 74LS138 provides negative going pulses when active. Additionally, in order to limit the current through the LEDs, a resistor may be needed in series with the transistor base connection and in series with each of the port B outputs.

The LEDs can be discrete Light Emitting Diodes or they can be 7 segment displays, wherein seven LEDs are connected to produce a stylised figure-8 with an additional LED for a decimal point (**Fig 4.10**).

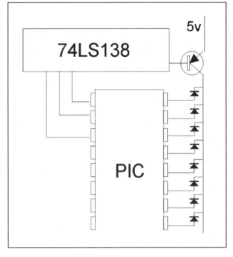

Fig 4.9: Using a transistor for increased currents

All of the numbers from zero to nine can be formed by switching on various combinations of the 7 LEDs. The 74LS138 allows up to 8 digits to be used in a numeric display (although only four are shown in the example shown in **Fig 4.11**).

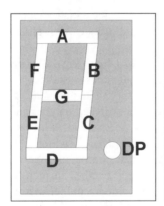

Fig 4.10: A seven segment chip

Port B Bit 0	Segment E
Port B Bit 1	Segment D
Port B Bit 2	Segment C
Port B Bit 3	Segment DP
Port B Bit 4	Segment B
Port B Bit 5	Segment A
Port B Bit 6	Segment F
Port B Bit 7	Segment G

Table 4.2: Bit connections

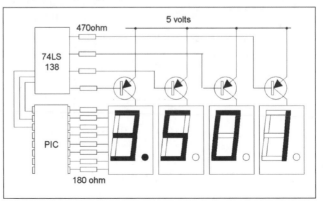

Fig 4.11: Driving seven segment displays

Here, the 74LS138 is connected to port A bits 0 to 2 and to the seven segment displays to port B. Common anode displays are used. The algorithm to drive the displays will depend on which segment of the display is connected to which bit of the interface. I tend to use the following arrangement.

A table read subroutine is used to convert a number into the appropriate digits (**Listing 4.6**). It works with numbers up to 15. Numbers above 9 are converted to their hexadecimal equivalents (A to F).

This routine is called with the number in the W register and it returns with the segment code in W. It assumes that a logic zero is needed to switch a segment on.

(Note that the word TABLE or any word starting with TABLE is reserved in MPASM and must not be used in a program. It can, however, be used with TASM)

If this table is not within the first 256 instructions of the program, the PCLATH register (register 0x0A in any register bank) must be set before calling this subroutine.

The routine works by adding the number to the current Program Counter register (register PCL is 0x02 in any register bank). In all cases, the decimal point is switched off.

The routine that drives the display is shown in **Listing 4.7**. In this routine, eight digits are used. These are held in registers 0x20 to 0x27, with register 0x20 being the left hand digit. Register DP contains the position of the decimal point and register DIGIT contains the number of the digit that is currently being displayed. The subroutine called TABLE is the same subroutine that was given earlier in this section.

This routine should be called every millisecond or so, in order to see an apparently stable display.

Listing 4.6: Table read

```
XTABLE  ANDLW   0x0F        ;And with 0x0F to limit to 0-15
        ADDWF   PCL, F      ;Add to current location (+ 1)
        RETLW   0x88        ;0
        RETLW   0xEB        ;1
        RETLW   0x4C        ;2
        RETLW   0x49        ;3
        RETLW   0x1B        ;4
        RETLW   0x19        ;5
        RETLW   0x18        ;6
        RETLW   0xCB        ;7
        RETLW   0x08        ;8
        RETLW   0x0B        ;9
        RETLW   0x0A        ;A
        RETLW   0x38        ;b
        RETLW   0x9C        ;C
        RETLW   0x68        ;d
        RETLW   0x1C        ;E
        RETLW   0x1E        ;F
```

```
MOVLW       0xFF            ;Turn out all LEDs
MOVWF       PORTB
INCF        DIGIT, W        ;Move to next digit
ANDLW       0x07            ;Limit to 8 digits (0-7)
MOVWF       DIGIT
MOVWF       PORTA           ;Update 74LS138
ADDLW       0x20            ;Add 0x20 to digit
MOVWF       0x04            ;Place in FSR register
MOVF        0x00, W         ;Read INDR register to get data
CALL        XTABLE          ;Call translate table
MOVWF       PORTB           ;Turn on number
MOVF        DP, W           ;Get Decimal point position
XORWF       DIGIT, W        ;Is it same as digit position?
BTFSS       STATUS, ZERO
RETURN                      ;No, so return
MOVLW       0xF7            ;Yes, so switch on decimal point
ANDWF       PORTB, F
RETURN
```

Listing 4.7: Display update routine

Binary to digit conversions

PIC peripherals, such as counters and A/D converters, use binary. So the result of a count using Timer 1 could result in register 0x0E containing 0x04 and register 0x0F containing 0x74 (7404 hexadecimal is equal to 29700). Before this can be output to a display, such as the one described above, it must be converted into single digits. One of the easiest ways to do this is as follows:

- Shift each digit register left by one bit.
- Do a bit test on bit 7 of the binary register. If it is a logic one, add one to the lowest decimal digit.
- Check if that digit now contains more than nine. The easiest way to check this is to add 6 and place the result in the W register. Now AND with 0x0F, and if the result is not zero then the total is ten or more. If it is, subtract ten from the register but add one to the next digit. Repeat until all digits have been checked.
- Get next bit of the binary register by shifting binary register left.
- Continue until all eight bits of the byte have been handled.

Like the display routine, it assumes that the data for the digits is to be placed in consecutive registers and that these registers have been cleared if necessary before starting. For multi-byte numbers such as those generated by Timer 1, call the routine separately for each byte, starting with the most significant byte (0x0F in the above example) and do not clear the registers before calling the routine with subsequent bytes.

The routine in **Listing 4.8** converts an 8 bit binary number into an 8 digit binary coded decimal (BCD) number. In this case, the BCD number is one that uses a byte for a single digit in the range 0 to 9. As with previous examples, the registers 0x20 to 0x27 are used to hold the BCD numbers with 0x20 holding the left hand (or most significant) digit. To change the number of digits, change the register called REGS and to change the base address of the registers, change the register

(Opposite) Listing 4.8: Binary to BCD procedure

```
BIN2BCD   MOVLW     0x07              ;Set number of bits to 7 (8 bits)
          MOVWF     BITS
          MOVLW     0x07              ;Set number of digits to 7 (8 digits)
          MOVWF     REGS
          MOVLW     0x20              ;Set base address for digit registers
          MOVWF     BASE
          GOTO      BINENTRY


BITLOOP   MOVF      REGS, W           ;Get current digit number
          ADDWF     BASE, W           ;Add to base to get register number
          MOVWF     FSR               ;Write to FSR
          CALL      SHIFTER           ;Call subroutine to shift this digit
          MOVF      REGS, F           ;Check if last digit
          BTFSC     STATUS, ZERO
          GOTO      NXTREG            ;Yes, so go to next bit of DATABYTE
          DECF      REGS, F           ;No so decrement digit number
          GOTO      BITLOOP           ;Go to next digit of this bit
NXTREG    MOVLW     0x07              ;Reset to right hand digit
          MOVWF     REGS
          MOVF      BITS, F           ;Check if last bit
          BTFSC     STATUS, ZERO
          RETURN                      ;Yes so return
          RLF       DATABYTE, F       ;No so shift binary number
          DECF      BITS, F           ;Decrement number of bits still to do
BINENTRY  CLRF      ADDONE            ;ADDONE=0 if DATABYTE bit 7 = 0
          BTFSC     DATABYTE, 7       ;or ADDONE=1 if DATABYTE bit 7 = 1
          INCF      ADDONE, F
          GOTO      BITLOOP           ;Continue with right hand digit


SHIFTER   BCF       STATUS, CARRY     ;Clear carry bit
          RLF       INDR, F           ;Rotate (multiply by two)
          MOVF      ADDONE, W         ;Add local carry bit
          ADDWF     INDR, F
          CLRF      ADDONE            ;Clear local carry bit
          MOVLW     0x06              ;Add 6 to total & put in W
          ADDWF     INDR, W
          ANDLW     0xF0              ;Check if 16 or more
          BTFSC     STATUS, ZERO
          RETURN                      ;No so return
          MOVLW     0x0A              ;Yes so subtract 10
          SUBWF     INDR, F
          INCF      ADDONE, F         ;Add one to local carry bit
          RETURN                      ;Return
```

```
CLRF      0x20
CLRF      0x21
CLRF      0x22
CLRF      0x23
CLRF      0x24
CLRF      0x25
CLRF      0x26
CLRF      0x27
MOVF      0x0F, W        ;Most significant byte to DATABYTE
MOVWF     DATABYTE
CALL      BIN2BCD
MOVF      0x0E, W        ;Least significant byte to DATABYTE
MOVWF     DATABYTE
CALL      BIN2BCD
```

Listing 4.9: Calling the binary to BCD procedure for Timer 1

Listing 4.10: Calling the binary to BCD procedure for an A/D conversion

called BASE. The binary data is in a register called DATABYTE. Other registers needed are called ADDONE and BITS. The register called BITS contains the number of bits to be converted. This must be loaded with a value of 0x07 at the start of this routine, even if the byte contains fewer than 8 significant bits. In addition to these programmer defined registers, the routine uses INDR (register 0x00), STATUS (register 0x03) and FSR (register 0x04). In the STATUS register, the routine uses ZERO (bit 2) and CARRY (bit 0).

On entry, the routine initialises the BITS, REGS and BASE registers before going to BINENTRY. This initialises ADDONE to zero if bit 7 of DATABYTE is clear, or to a one if bit 7 of DATABYTE is a logic one. The routine works from the right hand digit to the left, so register numbers are decremented. The actual shifting, checking if the digit is more than 9 and adding one where the previous digit was more that 9, is done by another subroutine called SHIFTER.

Converting an 8 bit binary number will take approximately 1.1ms.

```
CLRF      0x20
CLRF      0x21
CLRF      0x22
CLRF      0x23
CLRF      0x24
CLRF      0x25
CLRF      0x26
CLRF      0x27
BSF       3, 5           ;Go to register bank 1
MOVF      0x1E, W        ;Most significant byte to DATABYTE
BCF       3, 5           ;Go back to register bank 0
MOVWF     DATABYTE
CALL      BIN2BCD
MOVF      0x1E, W        ;Least significant byte to DATABYTE
MOVWF     DATABYTE
CALL      BIN2BCD
```

To use this routine with Timer 1, you must run the timer for an appropriate period and then run **Listing 4.9**.

For a 10 bit A/D conversion, bit 7 of register 0x1F in register bank 1 must be set to a logic 1 as part of the A/D initialisation procedure. This places the most significant two bits in one register and the least significant eight bits in another (**Listing 4.10**).

Alphanumeric displays

Although seven segment displays are good for displaying numeric data, they cannot display true text. For that, an alphanumeric display is needed. These units use Liquid Crystal Display (LCD) technology and can be purchased with up to 160 characters in multiple lines. Typical of these units are:

- Hitachi HD44780 and HD44100
- Samsung KS0066
- Sanyo LC7985 NA
- Epson SED1278
- UMC UM3881B
- OKI MSM6222

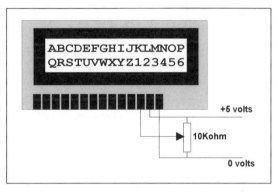

Fig 4.12: Contrast control

There may be some differences between models so care must be taken when selecting a suitable unit. The units that I use are manufactured by Display Elektronik GmbH and the retailer claims that they are compatible with the Hitachi HD44780 and HD44100 units.

These units have an on-board processor that requires a DC power supply of +5 volts to pin 2 and zero volts at pin 1. Pin 3 is a contrast voltage, which is normally about 4 volts below the supply voltage. This means that, with a 5 volt supply, the voltage on pin 3 is likely to be about 1 volt. However, experience shows that it is worthwhile making this voltage variable and I use a 10kΩ potentiometer or preset for this purpose (**Fig 4.12**).

The other 11 pins provide a bi-directional interface. This means that the display can be read from as well as written to, so there is no need for the PIC to keep copies of data that is displayed on the screen. Display units with more than 80 characters in total, and those with built in back-lights, may have extra pins. Pin assignments for displays with more than 80 characters also vary (See **Table 4.3**).

Pin	80 characters or less	More than 80 char
1	0 volts	Bit 7
2	5 volts	Bit 6
3	Contrast	Bit 5
4	Command (0) or Data (1)	Bit 4
5	Write (0) or Read (1)	Bit 3
6	Strobe (1)	Bit 2
7	Bit 0	Bit 1
8	Bit 1	Bit 0
9	Bit 2	Strobe (1) for first 80 char
10	Bit 3	Write (0) or Read (1)
11	Bit 4	Command (0) or Data (1)
12	Bit 5	Contrast
13	Bit 6	5 volts
14	Bit 7	0 volts
15	Not present	Strobe (1) for 2nd 80 char

Table 4.2: Pin assignments

The following descriptions apply only to displays with 80 characters or less.

Pin 5 is the read/write pin. If the program never reads from the display, this pin can be permanently wired to zero volts. Otherwise, the choice is between using all eight interface bits or only interface bits 4 to 7. In the case where a four bit interface is used, twice the number of transfers will of course be required. I prefer the 8 bit interface and tend to use port B for the data and port C for the strobe, read/write and data/command signals (see **Fig 4.13**). I use bits 5 to 7 of port C if I am not using the USART or bits 3 to 5 otherwise. Unless otherwise stated, the examples in this section use port B for data, bit 5 of port C for the strobe, bit 4 of port C for read/write and bit 3 of port C for command/data.

Four bit interfaces can use as few as six PIC interface port bits if read/write is not needed (**Fig 4.14**). This is normally the case as it is unusual to read data back from the display.

The procedure for transferring data and commands to the display is to place the information on the data line, then set the read/write and command/data lines. Then the strobe line is raised to a logic one for a short period before clearing it back to a logic zero. For example, the routine in **Listing 4.11** transfers a character (such as a letter A) to the display. It is assumed that the character is in the W register at the start of the routine:

For the 4 bit interface (using 6 lines), the data must first be stored temporarily in a register (**Listing 4.12**).

Notice the delays. For data, the strobe line must remain high for at least 220ns and low for at least 280ns. For PIC chips running a 20MHz clock, this is more than a single instruction. Therefore, additional NOP instructions have been added to provide the delay. However, having strobed the character into the display, the display takes about 40µs to process it.

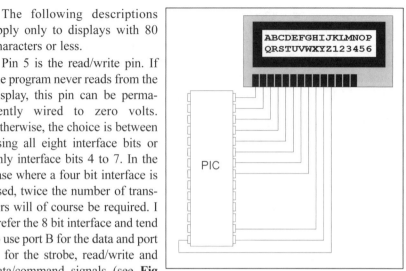

Fig 4.13: Connecting to PIC in 8 bit mode

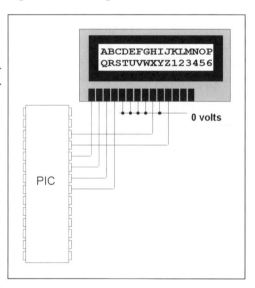

Fig 4.14: Connecting to PIC in 4 bit mode

```
WD8     MOVWF       PORTB           ;Move data to port B
        BSF         PORTC, 3        ;Set command/data to data
        BCF         PORTC, 4        ;Set read/write to write
        BSF         PORTC, 5        ;Raise strobe line
        NOP                         ;Delay (min 220nS)
        BCF         PORTC, 5        ;Lower strobe line
        NOP                         ;Delay (min 280nS)
        NOP
        RETURN
```

Listing 4.11: Writing to the display in 8 bit mode

```
WD4     MOVWF       TEMP            ;Store data (eg 0x41) in temp
        SWAPF       TEMP, W         ;Get bits 4-7 as bits 0-3 in W (eg
0x14)
        ANDLW       0x0F            ;Remove left hand 4 bits(eg 0x04 stays
in W)
        MOVWF       PORTB           ;Move data to port B
        BSF         PORTB, 4        ;Set command/data to data
        BSF         PORTB, 5        ;Raise strobe line
        NOP                         ;Delay (min 220nS)
        BCF         PORTC, 5        ;Lower strobe line
        NOP                         ;Delay (min 280nS)
        NOP
        MOVF        TEMP, W         ;Move data from temp to W (eg 0x41)
        ANDLW       0x0F            ;Remove left hand 4 bits(eg 0x01 stays
in W)
        MOVWF       PORTB           ;Move data to port B
        BSF         PORTB, 4        ;Set command/data to data
        BSF         PORTB, 5        ;Raise strobe line
        NOP                         ;Delay (min 220nS)
        BCF         PORTC, 5        ;Lower strobe line
        NOP                         ;Delay (min 280nS)
        NOP
        RETURN
```

Listing 4.12: Writing to the display in 4 bit mode

Commands also require time. For most commands a 40µs delay is adequate but for a Clear Screen or a return Cursor to Home Position command, a delay of about 1.5ms is needed.

These figures are normal and I have not found any displays that do not work with them, but the theoretical maximums are 53µs and 2.16ms. However, there is an even more important delay and that is the power up delay for the display unit, which is 30ms.

If an attempt is made to control the display before this time has elapsed then all commands and data are likely to be ignored. The command set is shown in **Table 4.4**.

Command	Bit 7	Bit 6	Bit 5	Bit 4	Bit 3	Bit 2	Bit 1	Bit 0	Time
Function Set *	0	0	1	I/F	Lines	1	0	0	40µS
Display on/off	0	0	0	0	1	1	Cursor	Blink	40µS
Clear Display	0	0	0	0	0	0	0	1	1.5mS
Entry Mode	0	0	0	0	0	1	I/D	SH	40µS
Return Cursor to Home	0	0	0	0	0	0	1	0	1.5mS
Cursor/Display Shift	0	0	0	1	SC	RL	0	0	40µS
Set Cursor Address	0	0	1	X	X	X	X	X	40µS

Table 4.4: Display commands

Notes:

- When using the 4 bit interface, bits 4 to 7 must be repeated (see below and Table 4.4).
- I/F is set to 1 for an 8 bit interface and 0 for a 4 bit interface
- Lines is set to 1 for all lines or 0 for alternate lines (top line only or lines 1 and 3)
- Cursor is set to 1 for visible cursor or 0 for no visible cursor
- Blink is set to 1 for a blinking cursor or 0 for an underline cursor
- I/D is set to 1 to move the cursor right/display left or 0 to move the cursor left/display right
- SH is set to 1 to move the display or 0 to move the cursor
- SC is set to 1 to shift the display or 0 to move the cursor
- RL is set to 1 for a right hand move or 0 for a left hand move
- X is set to 1 or 0 to make up the position, or address, that the cursor should move to.
- The cursor marks the position on the display that characters will be entered.

As mentioned above, the Function Set command is slightly modified when using a 4 bit interface. It becomes:
- First transfer: 0 0 0 1
- Second transfer   0 0 0 1
- Third transfer   L 1 0 0, where L is the number of lines.

This is the only time when a part of a command needs to be repeated.

The display can, in effect, operate in one of two modes. In the first mode, characters are entered from the left and additional characters appear to the right of existing characters, just like they do when you are writing or typing a note.

This mode is good for displaying short messages such as "SWR Error", "Repeater Shift On" or "Tone = G". The other mode is a scrolling mode where the characters all move left by one position and the new character is entered in the space left on the right hand side. This mode is better for very long messages such as displaying a QSO.

The following code fragment sets up a 16 character display to operate in scrolling mode with a single line of text. It uses two external subroutines:
- DELAY40 is a 40µS delay
- DELAY1500 is a 1.5mS delay

Following the initialisation routine shown in **Listing 4.13**, data can be written to the display unit using the routine given earlier in this section. The character set for the display unit is shown in **Table 4.5**.

```
        MOVLW    0x30              Function Set (8 bit interface 1 line)
        MOVWF    PORTB
        CALL     STROBE
        CALL     DELAY40

        MOVLW    0x0F              ;Display On, blinking cursor on
        MOVWF    PORTB
        CALL     STROBE
        CALL     DELAY40

        MOVLW    0x01              ;Clear Display
        MOVWF    PORTB
        CALL     STROBE
        CALL     DELAY1500

        MOVLW    0x07              ;Entry Mode, display shifted
        MOVWF    PORTB
        CALL     STROBE
        CALL     DELAY40

        MOVLW    0x8F              ;Set Cursor to Position 16 (0x0F)
        MOVWF    PORTB
        CALL     STROBE
        CALL     DELAY40
        RETURN

STROBE  BCF      PORTC, 3          ;Set command/data to Command
        BCF      PORTC, 4          ;Set read/write to write
        BSF      PORTC, 5          ;Raise strobe line
        NOP                        ;Delay (min 220nS)
        BCF      PORTC, 5          ;Lower strobe line
        NOP                        ;Delay (min 280nS)
        NOP
        RETURN
```

0x20	Space	0x30	0	0x40	@	0x50	P	0x60	`	0x70	p
0x21	!	0x31	1	0x41	A	0x51	Q	0x61	a	0x71	q
0x22	"	0x32	2	0x42	B	0x52	R	0x62	b	0x72	r
0x23	#	0x33	3	0x43	C	0x53	S	0x63	c	0x73	s
0x24	$	0x34	4	0x44	D	0x54	T	0x64	d	0x74	t
0x25	%	0x35	5	0x45	E	0x55	U	0x65	e	0x75	u
0x26	&	0x36	6	0x46	F	0x56	V	0x66	f	0x76	v
0x27	'	0x37	7	0x47	G	0x57	W	0x67	g	0x77	w
0x28	(	0x38	8	0x48	H	0x58	X	0x68	h	0x78	x
0x29	)	0x39	9	0x49	I	0x59	Y	0x69	I	0x79	y
0x2A	*	0x3A	:	0x4A	J	0x5A	Z	0x6A	j	0x7A	z
0x2B	+	0x3B	;	0x4B	K	0x5B	[	0x6B	k	0x7B	{
0x2C	,	0x3C	<	0x4C	L	0x5C	¥	0x6C	l	0x7C		
0x2D	-	0x3D	=	0x4D	M	0x5D	]	0x6D	m	0x7D	}
0x2E	.	0x3E	>	0x4E	N	0x5E	^	0x6E	n	0x7E	→
0x2F	/	0x3F	?	0x4F	O	0x5F	_	0x6F	o	0x7F	←

Listing 4.13: Initialising the display in 8 bit mode

Table 4.5: Display character set (the code on the left and character on the right)

Line no	Character Address (Hexadecimal)															
First	00	01	02	03	04	05	06	07	08	09	0A	0B	0C	0D	0E	0F
Second	40	41	42	43	44	45	46	47	48	49	4A	4B	4C	4D	4E	4F
Third	10	11	12	13	14	15	16	17	18	19	1A	1B	1C	1D	1E	1F
Fourth	50	51	52	53	54	55	56	57	58	59	5A	5B	5C	5D	5E	5F

Table 4.6: Display addressing

Notice the lack of a UK Pounds sign. Whilst this may be a problem in some applications, it is unlikely to have any major problems in radio related applications. Codes below 0x20 and above 0x7F are likely to produce Japanese characters. The exception to this rule is 0xFF (all logic ones) which produces a solid black block ■.

When reading to or writing from the display it is important to understand how the character addresses work, as the lines are not contiguous. Strange effects can occur if care is not taken. Although the first row of characters starts at address 0x00, as would be expected, the second row of characters always starts at address 0x40 irrespective of the number of characters on the first line. In addition, the third line is a continuation of the first line and the fourth line is a continuation of the second.

For example, a display with 4 lines of 16 characters will have an addressing scheme as shown in **Table 4.6**.

This means that if a program writes to the first line and gets to the end of the line, it will start to write into the third line. If it continues to write, then when it gets to the end of the second line there will be a very long delay before it starts to write into the second line. When scrolling the data, stranger effects can occur as data disappears from the screen only to reappear on a different line some time later.

Digital to analogue converters

Although some PICs have built-in Analogue to Digital Converters, none have built in Digital to Analogue (D/A) converters so these must be constructed by using a port on the PIC and external components.

D/A converters can be used for a variety of purposes, such as:

- Supplying a reference voltage to power supplies
- Generating CTCSS or test tones
- Recreating digitised speech.

The PIC itself does not have enough memory to hold speech, but it can take data from a computer link and recreate that. Alternatively, the

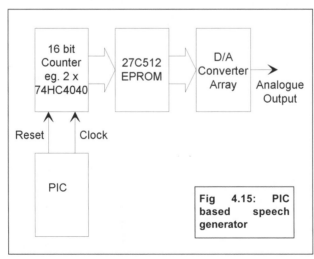

Fig 4.15: PIC based speech generator

Fig 4.16: Direct PIC D/A conversion

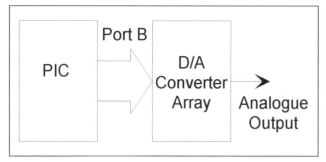

PIC can use external memory devices. At least 8kbyte of memory is required for each second of reasonable quality speech. For example, a 27C512 EPROM can hold up to 8 seconds of speech (**Fig 4.15**).

With a repeating waveform, such as a CTCSS tone, the PIC does not need to hold a lot of data and so it can drive the converter array directly. The same thing applies to slow moving signals, such as control signals to power supplies, which can be calculated by the PIC (**Fig 4.16**).

There are two ways to configure a D/A converter array:

1. As a voltage driven array where each resistor is double (or half) of the adjoining resistor (**Fig 4.17**).
2. As a current driven array, using just two values of resistors (**Fig 4.18**).

The voltage driven array has the advantage that it produces a full voltage range, from zero to the supply voltage, but it has the disadvantage of needing precision resistors and these can be very hard for an amateur to find. Current driven arrays on the other hand need only two resistor values, one of which is twice the value of the other. This is readily achieved by using three resistors of equal value R, with two of them connected either in series to give 2xR, or in parallel to give R/2. However, current driven arrays will only generate a signal that ranges from one half of the supply voltage up to the supply voltage. For signals such as speech and sine waves, this is not a problem as the signal will

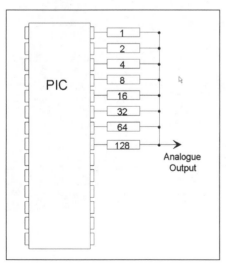

Fig 4.17: Voltage driven D/A array

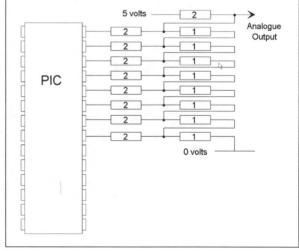

Fig 4.18: Current driven D/A array

probably be AC coupled and amplified anyway but DC signals are likely to require an operational amplifier (op amp) with a suitable gain and offset voltage (**Fig 4.19**).

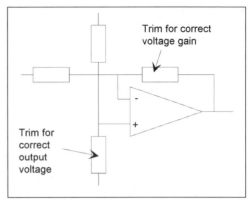

So far, the resistor values given in this section have been relative values. There is considerable scope for choosing values from the resistors that you have to hand. For example, for a current driven array, I have used values from 500Ω (2 x 1kΩ in

Figure 4.19: Operational Amplifier

parallel) to 20kΩ (2 x 10kΩ) in series. Do not be tempted to use values that are not 2:1 such as 2.2kΩ and 4.7kΩ or 4.7kΩ and 10kΩ as these produce distorted waveforms. For the op amp, a 1kΩ resistor and a 10kΩ preset are what I use to set the gain.

To generate a sine wave, the program has to output values at regular intervals. This interval must be at least twice the frequency of the required waveform. This means that if the PIC outputs a value to the port every 100μs (10,000 times per second) the maximum frequency is 5kHz. For speech, the output rate must be at least 8,000 samples per second. However, the output signal is a series of steps rather than a smooth signal (see photo) and it may need filtering before use. The closer that the switching frequency is to the required frequency, the harder this filtering is likely to be. For example, a CTCSS tome that is being generated by a PIC that is outputting a new signal to the port every 2.5ms (400Hz) will be harder to filter than a PIC that switches every 100μs.

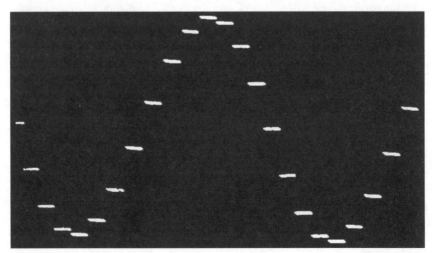

Digitally generated sine wave

5

PIC compilers and programmers

here are many compilers available for the 16 series PIC chips and these vary in sophistication from being fairly simple to having very extensive facilities. However, in general, they all have the ability to name registers, to name locations for GOTO and CALL instructions and they all use the same codes for the instructions. So an ADDWF is always an ADDWF. This means that there is an apparent 'sameness' about them - until you come to try and compile a program. Then the differences show up.

A typical program starts with register declarations. This is where the programmer names registers to make the task of writing the program easier. Most compilers limit the length of these strings to 32 characters but some have lower limits. Generally, names are case sensitive. So portb, Portb and PortB are three different things. However, I would never rely on this and consider it bad programming to give register names that vary only in that some letters are capitals. There are also limits on the characters that can be used in the names. None seem to like dashes (minus signs) in names such as "slow-clock" but most like underlines (slow_clock). In all cases, names must be declared before they are used but most compilers accept declarations part way through the code and at the start of subroutines. Declarations must start in column one (by the left hand margin) of each line. The general command is:

```
Label   EQU   number
```

You can use spaces or tabs between the elements (label - equ - number) but you must put some sort of gap there. In addition, you can declare bit numbers as well as declaring register numbers.

TASM requires a dot before the 'equ' (as in .EQU) and the 'equ' can be in upper or lower case. It will also take the number to be decimal unless specifically stated otherwise, whereas MPASM will assume that the number is hexadecimal and will not accept a dot before the 'equ'.

After the declarations comes an 'origin' statement. This tells the compiler where in memory the program will go. Again, TASM requires a dot in front of the command and assumes that numbers are decimal whereas MPASM will not accept a dot and assumes that numbers are hex.

The program comes next. Apart from numbers there are no apparent differences between instructions. If a location is named (or labelled) so that it can be referred to in a CALL or GOTO instruction then when the name is used for the location it must go in column one. Semi-colons mark the start of a comment (unlike other languages where they are often used to mark the end of a line) and you can only put one instruction on each line.

At the end of the program, you will need an END command. TASM requires a dot in from of the command (.END) and an extra blank line following it. However, if there is anything after the end command, TASM will continue to compile it. MPASM, on the other hand, does not need a dot or a blank line and it will stop compiling as soon as it reaches the END command.

There is one final difference. MPASM can accept commands to program EEPROM and to configure the oscillator, watchdog timer and similar items on the chip. With TASM, these aspects are handled by the chip loading program.

Using multiple files

Some programmers like to split large programs into multiple files, for example by keeping subroutines in their own files. Personally, I do not like to do this as I find it difficult to keep control over what register numbers I have used for what purpose. The exception to this rule is for the standard PIC register names and bit names. This is often referred to as a header or include file. The example in **Fig 5.1** is a small part of the include file for the 16F84 that is included with MPASM.

I have not used include files with any of the routines in this book as I prefer to show the full workings of every program.

Listing 5.1: Sample from header file

To include a file into another program, simply use the command #include "filename". The filename must be complete, including any suffix, and it must be

```
W                              EQU      H'0000'
F                              EQU      H'0001'
;----- Register Files-----------------------------------------------
--
INDF                           EQU      H'0000'
TMR0                           EQU      H'0001'
PCL                            EQU      H'0002'
STATUS                         EQU      H'0003'
FSR                            EQU      H'0004'
PORTA                          EQU      H'0005'
PORTB                          EQU      H'0006'
EEDATA                         EQU      H'0008'
EEADR                          EQU      H'0009'
PCLATH                         EQU      H'000A'
INTCON                         EQU      H'000B'
;----- STATUS Bits -------------------------------------------------
--
IRP                            EQU      H'0007'
RP1                            EQU      H'0006'
RP0                            EQU      H'0005'
NOT_TO                         EQU      H'0004'
NOT_PD                         EQU      H'0003'
Z                              EQU      H'0002'
DC                             EQU      H'0001'
C                              EQU      H'0000'
```

in speech (quotation) marks. It does not need to have a .asm suffix, you can use whatever suffix you wish to use. The file will be included at that point, exactly as if you had copied it there. The file that you have included in your main program can itself include other files. Indeed, include files can be nested in this way up to five files deep. In addition, it does not matter if a register is declared many times as long as the declaration is the same in all cases.

However, please note that if the same name is used for two different registers then the compiler will complain, but if two names are used for the same register, it will not. This means that if one file names register 20 as "slow_clock" and uses it to keep a timer loop, but an included file declares register 20 as "switch_status" then the program will compile correctly even though two different parts of the program are trying to do entirely different things with the same register. This is the main reason why I do not like using included files.

Identifying and converting programs

If you find an interesting PIC program on the web or in a magazine, you may be tempted to compile and use it. However, very often you will find that your compiler just complains and gives a very long list of errors.

The first task in trying to successfully compile an unknown program is to ascertain for which compiler it has been written. Look for dots in front of the "equ" of any declarations. If they are there then it is probably a TASM program but if they are missing it is probably MPASM. Now look for any "include" statements. This indicates that the program is not complete. If the include files name a PIC chip type then the include file is probably just a list of standard PIC registers and you can probably download the file from the Microchip web site. However, if you have a copy of MPASM then you may already have it.

Once you have the correct compiler and the correct include files, the program should compile. Note that there is no difference in the compiler for 16 series chip types. A compiler for a 16C55 will also compile compile a program for a 16F946 and vice versa. Both will compile programs for 16CR72, 16HV540 and 16F648 chips as well as for standard chip types like the 16F84 and 16F873.

If you find that your compiler is different to the compiler that the program was written for then you may need to convert the program. The most important aspect is the number types and how they are identified. For example, MPASM identifies hexadecimal numbers with 0x or H in front of the number, whilst TASM uses $ in front of the number or a lower-case 'h' after the number.

MPASM also has a number of reserved names that must not be used within a program. These names include 'space', 'table', 'start' and 'end'.

Once the dots have been added (or removed), numbers have been converted (remembering the differences between numbers that have no identifier), reserved names removed and any include files added, the error messages produced by the compiler should start to become meaningful. The compiler produces messages when it detects an error, but this is not necessarily where the error is. Very often, the actual error is a line or two before the location that the compiler reports. TASM places its error reports onto the screen and into the list file. This file has a .LST extension suffix. It can be opened in any text editor, such as Notepad to yield a memory address and the numeric code that the PIC needs. It then gives the instruction that it has translated. It is always worth

The PIC for computer programmers

Experienced computer programmers often have difficulties moving to PIC chips, particularly those who have learned on modern computer languages such as 'C', 'C++' and Java. If you are not a computer programmer, please skip this panel.

Firstly, there is the issue of memory size. With most computers memory sizes are measured in megabytes, whereas PIC memories are often only a couple of kilobytes. Then there is the lack of data storage - only 68 bytes in a 16F84. This makes it difficult to build strings in data memory, and arrays are out of the question.

Then there is the way that program flow is programmed. Modern programmers learn recursive programming techniques and are taught that the use of 'go to' statements is the mark of a bad programmer - but with the PIC, 'GOTO' and 'CALL' (call subroutine) are the only options.

There is no FOR statement that will run a loop for a certain number of times. You, the programmer, must build up these statements by, for example, subtracting the finish condition from the current loop number (being careful not to store the result back in the register) and checking whether the result is still positive.

When writing programs for the PIC, some commands must start at the left (column 1) of a line and others must not. This is also different to most computer languages, which disregard white spaces such as tabs.

However, probably the biggest issue is one of scope. With computer languages, when a variable is used in a subroutine (or function as they are normally called these days), it is not necessarily available to the main program or to another subroutine. This means that the programmer does not need to worry about whether the same name has been used in a different part of the program. It also makes it easy to take subroutines from one program to another. With the PIC, all names are global. In addition, it is the programmer and not the compiler that assigns variables to real world register locations. This makes it very difficult to keep a library of subroutines that can be called when compiling different programs.

Indeed, although the process of writing and compiling PIC programs has some similarities with computer programming, it is probably best to treat it as being an entirely separate discipline and not to assume anything until you have tested it and know that it works.

looking back up the listing to see if there are any instruction lines (not command lines or declarations) that do not have a code against them. This is probably where the error is. The .OBJ file, that TASM also produces, is the final completed machine code program.

MPASM does not list errors but places them in a file with a .ERR extension. Like TASM, it also places error messages in a list (.LST) file. The final completed machine code program is placed in a .OBJ file.

Programming the chip

TASM can produce code in either binary or Intel hex format. MPASM can only produce code in Intel hex format. Neither of these formats is what the chip needs when it is being programmed. Therefore, also required is a loader program, that takes the code in Intel hex, binary or some other form, and converts it into the form that the chip needs. To make matters worse, different PIC chip types require programming differently. This difference is subtle and you need to take into account both the chip number *and the suffix*. For example, the programming algorithm for a PIC16F873A-1/SP is different from that for a PIC16F873A-04/SP.

This difference has nothing to do with high and low voltage programming. It concerns the command codes and the amount of data that can be sent at any one time.

In normal programming mode, when the reset (MCLR) pin is raised to between about 12 to 14 volts, the chip invokes an internal resistor/capacitor oscillator and start a special "loader" program that is burned into the chip. This program reads (and has the ability to write to) bits 6 and 7 of port B. Bit 6 is a strobe or clock bit and bit 7 is for data. The bits are sent serially, one after another, and the clock bit strobes each bit between the chip and the programming equipment. This means that the interface will operate at almost any speed, but the chip does require time to actually write the data into the program memory, registers or EEPROM.

Low voltage programming

Some chips have a "low voltage programming" mode. This does not require a high voltage supply. +5 volts is placed on the MCLR pin, with bit 3 of port B held at zero volts. Bit 3 of port B is then raised to 5 volts and this sets the chip into programming mode. Once the chip is in programming mode, it responds to the same commands as for high voltage programming. However it must be noted that, unless low voltage programming is disabled, pin 3 of port B can not be used for input/output purposes. In addition, once low voltage programming has been disabled it cannot be enabled again.

In-circuit programming

Even with high voltage programming, it is relatively easy to design PIC circuits so that the chips can be reprogrammed without removing them from their circuit board. This can be done either by placing a resistor is series with bit 6 and bit 7 of port B, if they are being used for inputs, or by using links (or switches) to disconnect them from the rest of their circuitry. In addition, a diode is needed in series with the MCLR pin. (If a reset circuit is used, a resistor should be placed in series with the diode). **Fig 5.1** refers.

Fig 5.1: In circuit programming

Programming hardware

Whether the chip is being programmed in-circuit or not, the program has been compiled on a computer and it needs to get from there and into the chip. Most programmers connect either through a parallel printer port or through a serial COM port.

Printer port programmers normally use bit 0 of the interface for data and bit 1 for the clock. Only a single 74LS07 chip is required to provide buffering. The photograph and **Fig 5.2** show my homebuilt programmer for the 16F84.

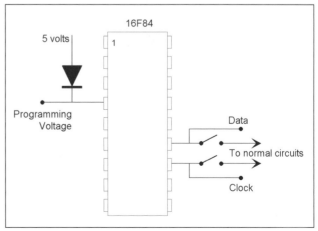

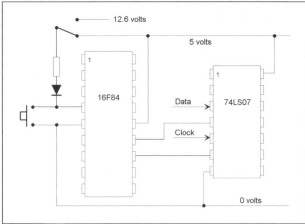

Home built programmer for 16F84 and . . .   **Fig 5.2: . . . the circuit diagram**

5 volts and 12 to 14 volts are also required. I use 12.6 volts, which I derive by placing a 4001 diode in series with the common line of a 7812 regulator (**Fig 5.3**).

The whole unit is built into a small plastic box.

Serial port interfaces use the RTS line for the clock and the DTR line for the data. With the standard 9 pin connector, pin 7 is clock (RTS) and pin 4 for data (DTR). 25 pin connectors use pin 4 for RTS (clock) and pin 20 (DTR) for data. Because computer serial ports use positive and negative voltages, these must be converted. This can be done either by using a MAX202 or MAX232 converter chip or by using a simple transistor converter. Almost any NPN transistor can be used. I use 2N3904 for the transistors and 1N4148 for the diodes.

Whatever type of programmer is used, please remember that it must be compatible with your programming software. The alternative is to buy a package of programming hardware plus the compiler and programming software from a single supplier but, if you are going to do this, please make sure that it will program the types of PIC that you want to use. However, even if it won't, you may be able to use a compatible chip type that it will program.

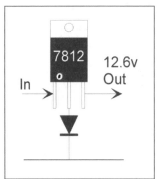

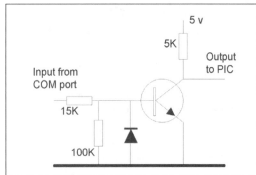

Fig 5.3: 12.6 volt regulator   **Fig 5.4: Voltage converter**

6

Projects: Introduction

here are many things that are common to the way that I build all of my projects so I thought it best to explain them here rather than in the individual projects.

Firstly, I don't claim any originality for the designs that are featured here. Many have been influenced by, or even had parts copied from, other designs that have featured in other RSGB and ARRL publications or featured on the Internet. In line with this sentiment, I would urge you to modify the design to suit your own requirements rather than slavishly follow my designs. To this end, I have specifically not given details for box cutting or case design.

Tools

None of these projects needs specialist tools apart from a PC and PIC programmer. The hardware can be constructed with hand tools such as junior hacksaws, hand drills, files and soldering irons. A hobby drill with cutting tools may make construction easier but it is by no means essential.

Circuit boards

I hate making Printed Circuit Boards and will avoid it wherever I can because of all those chemicals. If I have to do it then I will try to make one by cutting away the copper with my hobby drill but I much prefer to use ready made stripboard whenever I can.

If I need a ground plane then I back the stripboard with a piece of plain copper clad board.

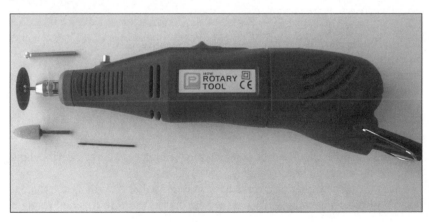

A hobby drill may make construction easier

Stripboard

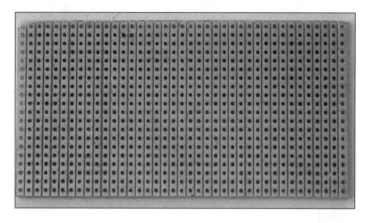

Full Listings

The complete program listing for each project can be found in the Appendix, and (together with other useful material) at www.rsgb.org/books /extra/picbasics.htm

Software

All listings given for these projects are written for 'assembly' using MPASM. If you are using TASM or another assembler/compiler, the programs will need modifying before the will compile. The main differences between compilers are the way that numbers are written and the command structure. With regard to numbers, MPASM defaults to hexadecimal and uses the prefix of "0x" (zero - ex) whereas TASM defaults to decimal and uses a dollar sign ($) to signify hexadecimal. Commands, such as EQU (equals) are prefixed by a dot (or decimal point) in TASM but are not prefixed in MPASM.

Voltage regulators

I always use three pin regulators in TO-220 style cases. These are available with current carrying capacities of between 0.5 Amps and 5 Amps. I use this type of chip because I like their physical presentation. The output and common (0 volt) wires are bent down and soldered to the board whereas the input line is bent up and the battery connector or the positive wire from the input socket is soldered directly to this pin. That way, 'dangerous' input voltages are kept away from

Mounting the voltage regulator

the chips. (The voltages are dangerous to the chips and not to people, as I always use low voltage converters to power my projects).

Seven segment arrays

This array can be expanded or contracted depending on the number of digits required for a particular project.

I use 0.5" displays because these have pins spaced at 0.6" along the top and bottom of the display chips. This allows the display chips to fit side by side in

40 pin integrated circuit type chip sockets. Each 40 pin socket can carry four digits so two sockets can carry up to 8 digits. For 8 digits it may be necessary to mount them on more than one piece of stripboard, as the standard boards that are available in the UK, have a maximum of 39 strips.

The main board is cut with the strips running vertically, in parallel with the short edge of the board. Three other boards are required and these have the strips running horizontally, along the length of the board. These boards should be slightly longer than the width of the main board. Two of these boards are four strips wide and one is only one strip wide. However, you can cut these slightly wider if you need to. The boards are mounted as shown on the diagram below with the insulated sides of the boards together. This means that, looking from the face of the digits, you can see the copper strips of the long thin boards. If you turn the composite board over, you can see the vertical copper strips of the main board. See **Fig 6.1**.

Boards are connected together by soldering links between the front and back boards in the positions shown. The only components required, apart from the displays and their holders, are some PNP transistors. One transistor is needed for each digit. The emitter of each transistor is connected to the single track strip to create a common positive rail. As long as the track is cut, between the emitter and collector, you can solder the emitter on both sides of the board. Track cuts are also required to prevent the base signal from going through to the display. Other track cuts are required behind the seven segment displays, leaving the centre pin of each digit intact. All track cuts are made to the main board.

I use pins to connect the digit drive signals, the segment drive signals and the common positive line.

Note that there is no negative or zero volt line with this seven segment display unit.

Fig 6.1: Seven segment display board

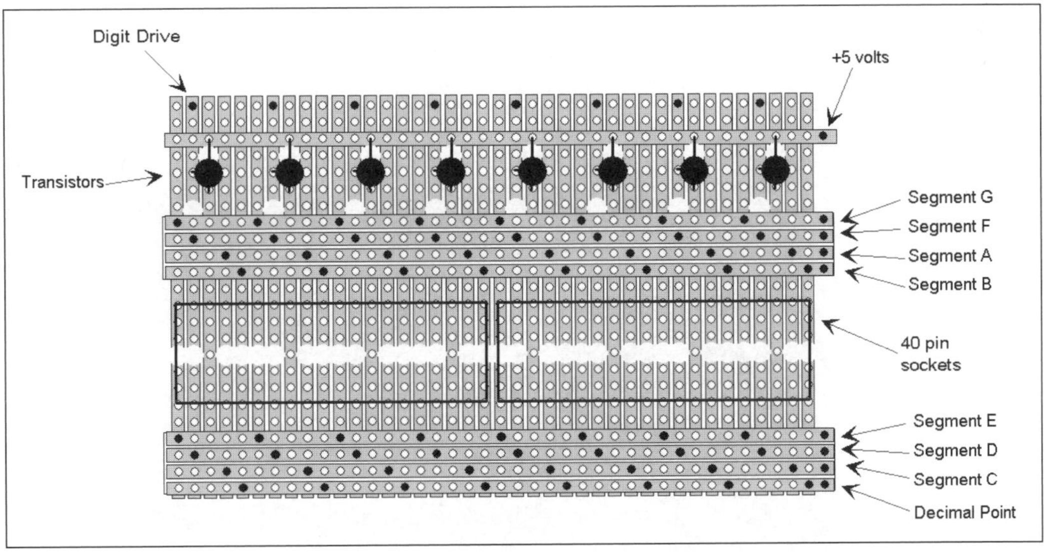

7

Project 1 - A clock for the shack

The British amateur radio licence states that the station log must record times using Universal Co-ordinated Time (UTC). Many Radio Amateurs also use UTC when arranging contacts and nets that involve amateurs from different time zones. In this context, UTC provides neutrality that avoids the need for the other person to work out what time zone you are in and to consider whether Daylight Saving Time (Summer Time) is being used. In addition, the start and end times of many radio contests are given in UTC.

Some amateurs have perfected the knack of translating times in their heads but I would often miss the first hour of a contest because I got the time wrong. I have tried using a normal clock that is set to UTC but, no matter how I mark the dial, I often end up glancing at the shack clock and thinking that I've got an extra hour to finish making contacts before collecting my wife from work. On numerous occasions, other people have told me that my clock is wrong and I have even had times where others have 'helped' me by setting my shack clock to the 'correct' time. I've even done it myself when the clocks change and I go round changing the time on all of our clocks and watches.

This clock overcomes these problems because it doesn't look like a clock. The letters 'UTC', which are incorporated in the display, make it look more like a piece of radio equipment. Although I've had people ask what it is, nobody has told me that the time is wrong or has tried to correct it.

Principles of operation

A 4MHz crystal provides the timing oscillator for the 16F84A PIC chip. This makes the PIC operate at a rate of one cycle per microsecond. Because the software is organised as a loop of exactly one thousand instruction cycles, the program loops every millisecond.

Within that millisecond, the program updates the time and drives the display.

The time is kept in a series of nested counters:

- Up to 5ms in 1ms increments
- Up to 1 second in 5ms increments
- Up to 1 minute in 1 second increments
- Up to 10 minutes in 1 minute increments
- Up to 1 hour in 10 minute increments
- Up to 10 hours in 1 hour increments
- Tens of hours in 10 hour increments
- Up to 24 hours in 1 hour increments. This counter is needed to reset the hours and tens of hours at the end of each day.

Counters that increment every minute, 10 minutes, hour and 10 hours are used for the display, along with PIC registers that contain the letters 'u', 't' and 'c'. The actual display is multiplexed. This means that no more than one digit is actually lit at any instant in time. It is the persistence of human vision that makes the digits all seem to be lit at the same time.

Within the one millisecond loop, the software:

- Switches off the digit that is currently lit
- Advances the display mechanism to the next digit
- Takes the contents of the relevant counter or register
- Translates this information into the code that switches on the appropriate segments
- Switches on the segments of the new digit.

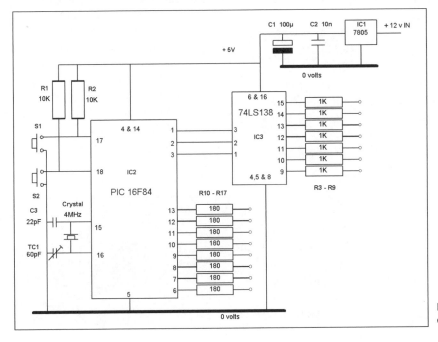

Fig 7.1: Circuit diagram

The hardware

The clock is built as two sub-units in a transparent red plastic case. Each sub-unit is built using stripboard. The circuit diagram is shown in **Fig 7.1**.

Because the display sub-unit is used in a number of different projects, it is described earlier in this book.

The PIC sub-unit is a single piece of 6cm (2.4in) high by 10cm (4in) strip-board with the strips running parallel to the longer side. Cut the strips as shown by using a spot face cutter or a drill bit. Next, add the wire links. Finally, mount the rest of the components including the IC sockets but do not mount the integrated circuits at this stage. Do not be tempted to mount the PIC directly onto the board as it will probably be necessary to remove the PIC for reprogramming before final assembly.

Carefully check the finished board and remove any short circuits before wiring the sub-units together. Then apply power and check for the correct voltages before inserting the 74138 and a programmed PIC.

Notes on components

Very few of the components are critical. The circuit draws up to 80mA but this could be regulated on the board using any suitable 5 volt regulator, or externally by using a regulated power supply.

Other types of PIC chip could probably be used without modifying the board. Examples include 16F711 and 16F628 although the author has not tested these. The type of 74138 is also not critical.

Capacitors C1 and C2 are simply there to provide stability so their values are not critical. C1, for example, could be any value over 10µF with more than 6 volt rating.

C2 should be in the range from 1nF to 470nF. The trimmer TC1 is used to adjust the crystal frequency. Select on test components could be used as an alternative.

Resistors R1 and R2 could be any value from 100Ω to 47kΩ. The other resistors could also be changed by a value or two (down to 470Ω for the 1kΩ and between 120Ω and 220Ω for the 180Ω). However, it is important that each bank of resistors is made up from identical resistors.

If a higher frequency crystal is used, this can be adjusted in software. Details are given later.

Component List	
IC1	L7805CV
IC2	PIC 16F84A
IC3	SN74LS138
C1	100µF 16V
C2	10nF
C3	22pF
TC1	60 or 65pF trimmer
R1, R2	10kΩ
R3-R9	1kΩ
R10-R17	180Ω
Crystal	4MHz
S1, S2	Push to Make switches
Misc.	18 pin IC holder
	14 pin IC holder
	Wire
	Pins (Optional)

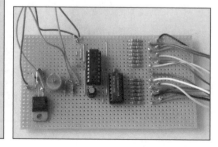

Component layouts

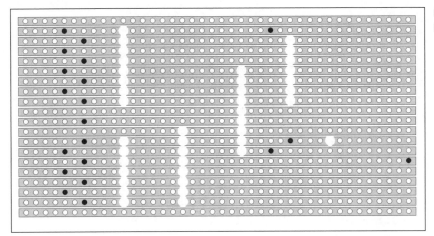

Fig 7.2: Cuts and pins (Bottom view)

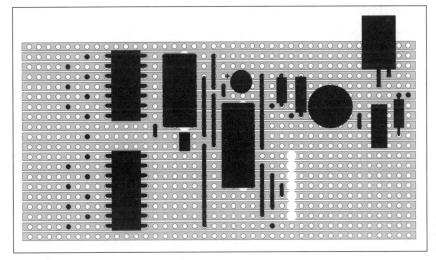

Fig 7.3: Wires and component layout (Top view)

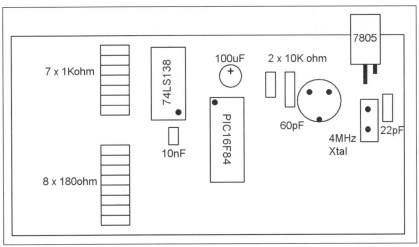

Fig 7.4: Component values

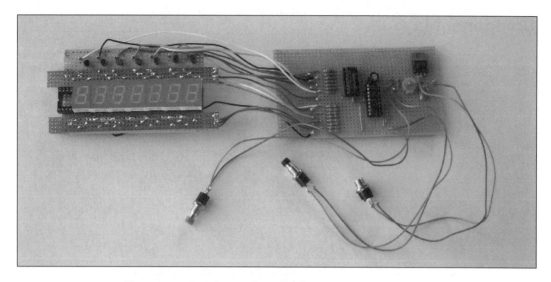

Programming the PIC

Before use, the PIC will need to be programmed. The process for compiling PIC programs and for programming PIC chips is described earlier in this book.

For this project, the configuration bits must be set for a high speed crystal oscillator and both the watchdog timer and power-up timer must be disabled.

Testing and adjusting the time

Once the PIC has been programmed, it can be fitted into the PIC sub-unit and power applied. Unless the source code has been changed, the clock should now read "12.00utc". If it does not, switch off and check the circuit for short circuits and for the correct voltages. When any faults have been corrected, switch on again.

If the clock is still not working, check it by using an oscilloscope, if you have one, or a multimeter set to DC. An active pin that is working correctly should give a meter reading somewhere above zero volts and below 5 volts depending on the length of time that it spends in either the one or the zero logic state.

Check the oscillator on pin 15. This should give a reading of about 2.5 Volts. If it is reading zero or 5 Volts then the oscillator is probably in the wrong mode and it will be necessary to reprogram the PIC, taking care to ensure that the configuration bits have been correctly set.

When the oscillator is running correctly, check the outputs on pins 1, 2, and 3. Pins 1 and 2 should give meter readings of about 2 volts. Pin 3 should give a reading of about half a volt. If any two of these pins are reading correctly then the PIC is incrementing the 74138. You can also check the output of the 74138 (pins 9 to 16). Each pin should read about 4 volts. Should the 74138 not be getting the correct signals from the PIC then it may be that it has been incorrectly programmed. Reprogram the chip ensuring that the Watchdog Timer is disabled.

If the 74138 is working correctly, check the PIC side of the cathode resistors. Each pin should be somewhere between 1 volt and 4 volts. An error here tends to indicate a short circuit or an error in the source code of the program. Check the source and recompile the program before reprogramming the PIC.

If the display is still not reading 12.00utc when the unit is switched on, check the inter-unit wiring and the display board. All of the active pins on the display chips should read between 1 and 4 volts with the anodes (pins 3 and 8 of each digit) reading the same or lower than the cathodes.

Once the clock is operating, the time can be set. If the hours or minutes are incrementing about one digit per second, check the hour and minute switches that are used to set the time, and their pull-up resistors. After a minute or so, the clock should advance to 12.01UTC. If it does not do this, check that the watch-dog timer was disabled when the PIC was programmed.

To change the time, press the hour or minute buttons as appropriate. This will advance the time at a rate of 1 hour (or 1 minute) per second.

Timekeeping can be adjusted through the hardware or through software. I have actually found it easier to make the adjustments through software but the choice is yours. Hardware changes are made by adjusting the variable capacitor in the oscillator circuit until the clock keeps the correct time.

To change the timekeeping in software it is necessary to know by how much the clock is out. Adjust the clock and note the time. Then leave the clock running for at least 18 to 24 hours before checking it again. The longer that the clock is left for, the more accurately it can be set.

Note the time and how many seconds the clock has lost or gained. Do this by noting when the minute figure changes. Now work out how many seconds the clock was running for and divide this figure by the number of seconds lost or gained. This will give you a figure that the clock is losing (or gaining) one second for every X seconds that it is run.

Load the source code into a text editor. If the clock is gaining time (running fast) it will be necessary to add NOP instructions. Remove NOP instructions to make the clock run faster. NOP instructions do nothing but use time. In practice, it is normally necessary to both add and remove NOP instructions. For example, if the clock is losing one second every 8.52 seconds, remove a NOP from the 1ms count. Then add 29 NOPs to the 5ms count and 3 NOPs to the 1s count. the clock should now keep the correct time.

Software operation

Note that anything that comes on a line after a semi-colon is a comment and does not affect the program in any way.

The source code starts by declaring some registers and bits (**Listing 7.1**). This simply makes the source code easier to read. For example, after declaring register 3 as the status register (STATUS .EQU 03) the program can use the word status rather than using the numeral 3.

Some registers and bits are internal to the PIC but the programmer defines others. Programmer (or user) registers in the 16F84 PIC start with register 11 (0x0B) and go to register 31 (0x1F). This program does not use all of these registers. Note that the display digits must go into consecutive registers. Other items could go into any user register.

The next directive (ORG) tells the compiler where to place the program in the PIC's memory. Because this program does not use interrupts, there is no program after the ORG 4 directive. The program itself starts at address 5.

Opposite. (Top) Listing 7.1: Defining registers. (Bottom) Listing 7.2: Initialising the ports

```
HRTWO     EQU     0x10    ;Count 0 - 2. Updated every 10 Hours. Left hand display digit.
HRTEN     EQU     0x11    ;Count 0 - 9. Updated every Hour. Second display digit.
MINSIX    EQU     0x12    ;Count 0 - 5. Updated every 10 Minutes. Third display digit.
MINTEN    EQU     0x13    ;Count 0 - 9. Updated every Minute. Fourth display digit.
LETU      EQU     0x14    ;Letter U. Fifth display digit.
LETT      EQU     0x15    ;Letter T. Sixth display digit.
LETC      EQU     0x16    ;Letter C. Seventh display digit.
BLANK     EQU     0x17    ;Unused eighth display digit.
COUNT     EQU     0x18    ;Count 0 - 200. Updated every 5mS
CNT2      EQU     0x19    ;Count 0 - 5. Updated every 1mS
SECS      EQU     0x1A    ;Count 0 - 59. Updated every 1mS
HOURS     EQU     0x1B    ;Count 0 - 23. Updated every Hour
CHAR      EQU     0x1C    ;Display Digit 0-7
DIGIT     EQU     0x1D    ;PortA Count (0-28 in 4's)
DELAY     EQU     0x1E    ;Delay Count
```

```
              BSF       STATUS, 5
              MOVLW     0x03
              MOVWF     PORTA           ;PORTA = Bits 2-5 = Output, 0-1 =
      Input
              CLRF      PORTB           ;PORTB = Output
              BCF       STATUS, 5
              CLRF      PCLATH
              CLRF      CHAR
              CLRF      DIGIT
              CLRF      COUNT
              CLRF      CNT2
              CLRF      SECS
              MOVLW     0x00
              MOVWF     MINTEN
              MOVLW     0x00
              MOVWF     MINSIX
              MOVLW     0x02
              MOVWF     HRTEN
              MOVLW     0x01
              MOVWF     HRTWO
              MOVLW     0x0C
              MOVWF     HOURS
              MOVLW     0x0A
              MOVWF     LETU
              MOVLW     0x0B
              MOVWF     LETT
              MOVLW     0x0C
              MOVWF     LETC
      TICK    MOVLW     0xFF
              MOVWF     PORTB           ;Clear Display
```

```
MOVF        DIGIT, W
ADDLW       0x04
ANDLW       0x1C              ;0x1C = 28
MOVWF       DIGIT
MOVWF       PORTA
```

Listing 7.3: Selecting the display digit

First, the port directions are set. Each bit on each port can act as an input or as an output. Sending a logic one to a bit sets that bit as an input. A zero makes the bit an output. In order to tell the port that this is a direction command, bit 5 must first be set in the status register (register 3). To go back to using the ports for data, bit 5 must be cleared from the status register.

The next task is to initialise the other registers (**Listing 7.2**). Many registers are simply cleared by using a CLRF command. Other registers are initialised to a different value by moving the value into the 'W' register (MOVLW) and then moving the 'W' register to another register. For example, MOVLW 0x0C followed by MOVWF HOURS puts the value 12 (0x0C) into the hours register (register 0x1B).

Having initialised the registers, the program goes into the 1ms loop. The name 'tick' on the left hand side of a line is a label. This allows the program to come back to this point when it needs to do so. Once again, the use of names means that programmers do not need to work out where in the PIC's memory this line will be stored.

The program's first task is to update the display. The cathodes are all set to 5 volts (MOVLW 0xFF and MOVWF PORTB) and then the anode count is updated.

Because the design uses bits 2, 3 and 4 of port A for the count, it needs to be incremented by four at a time.

The program then gets the actual character to display (**Listing 7.4**). It does this by getting the position register (CHAR) and incrementing it by one. Because there are only 7 digits, plus the unused eighth digit, the count is 'AND'ed with 7. This makes sure that the count cycles from 7 back to zero. Sixteen is then added because the first digit is in register 16. For example, tens of hours are in register 16, hours are in register 17, tens of minutes in register 18 and so on. If the digits are moved to a different series of registers, this value must be changed.

The actual value of the digit is obtained by placing the register number into the FSR register (register 4) and reading the INDR register (register 0). After

```
INCF        CHAR, W           ;Update character
ANDLW       0x07
MOVWF       CHAR
ADDLW       0x10              ;0x10 = 16
MOVWF       FSR
MOVF        INDR, W           ;Get value from register
ANDLW       0x0F              ;Reduce to value between 0 and 15
CALL        XTABLE            ;Convert to LED segments
MOVWF       PORTB             ;Output segment details to display
```

Listing 7.4: Displaying the character

```
XTABLE  ADDWF   PCL, F
        RETLW   0x01            ;Zero        0x01=1
        RETLW   0x57            ;One 0x57=87
        RETLW   0x22            ;Two 0x22=34
        RETLW   0x12            ;Three       0x12=18
        RETLW   0x54            ;Four        0x54=84
        RETLW   0x18            ;Five        0x18=24
        RETLW   0x08            ;Six 0x08=8
        RETLW   0x53            ;Seven       0x53=83
        RETLW   0x00            ;Eight       0x00=0
        RETLW   0x50            ;Nine        0x50=80
        RETLW   0x0F            ;10  =  "U"   0x0F15
        RETLW   0x2C            ;11  =  "T"   0x2C=44
        RETLW   0x2E            ;12  =  "C"   0x2E=46
        RETLW   0xFF            ;13  0xFF=255
        RETLW   0xFF            ;14  0xFF=255
        RETLW   0xFF            ;15  0xFF=255
        RETLW   0xFF            ;16  0xFF=255
```

Listing 7.5: Converting numbers to LED segments

another AND, to make sure that an error does not cause a calamity, the look-up table is called. This converts the value into a series of bits to drive the cathode. The actual table routine, which comes later in the program file, is in **Listing 7.5**.

(Note that the word TABLE or any word starting with TABLE is reserved in MPASM and must not be used in a program. It can, however, be used with TASM)

The digit value is added to the program counter (PCL - register 2). This causes the program to skip that many instructions. A zero causes the program to execute the next instruction whereas a five would skip five instructions and execute 'RETLW 0x18'. RETLW causes the program to return, carrying the appropriate value in the 'W' register. These values are inverted so a zero in a bit position will turn the light on and a one will turn it off. For example, 255 is all ones so no light will be on. 01 is all zeros except for the least significant bit so all of the lights will be on except one. In this case, it is the line across the middle of the displayed digit. Back in the calling program, this value is moved to port B.

Although it may seem that the program has done a lot, this has only taken 20µs so it is necessary to waste some time before doing anything else. Two counts are done. The first counts down from 201 (0xC9) to zero (**Listing 7.6**).

Each loop of the count takes 3µs so the complete loop takes 603µs, plus the 20µs to update the display giving a total time so far of 623µs. Another loop, of 121 x 3µs (363µs) follows to bring the total up to 986µs. The remaining 14µs (to bring the total up to 1000µs or 1ms) is taken up with adjusting the counters.

```
        MOVLW   0xC9            ;0xC9 = 201
        MOVWF   DELAY
LOOP1   DECFSZ  DELAY, F
        GOTO    LOOP1
```

Listing 7.6: Delay loop

```
    INCF        CNT2, F             ;End of 1ms loop
    MOVF        CNT2, W
    SUBLW       0x05
    BTFSS       STATUS, ZERO        ;5ms?
    GOTO        TICK                ;No
    CLRF        CNT2                ;Yes
```

Listing 7.7: 5ms loop

```
    BTFSS       PORTA, 0
    GOTO        INCMIN
    BTFSS       PORTA, 1
    GOTO        INCHR
```

Listing 7.8: Incrementing minutes and hours

Each counter is incremented before being moved into the 'W' register. The maximum value is subtracted from 'W' and a check made to see if the result is zero. If it is then the counter is reset to zero and the next counter is incremented. If the maximum value has not yet been reached, the program branches back to the start of the timing loop. **Listing 7.7** refers.

NOP instructions are added, at various locations, to slow the clock down. Additional NOP instructions can be added at these points to slow the clock further and so adjust it so that it keeps the correct time. To speed up the clock, reduce the value in the instruction "MOVLW 0x79", for example to read "MOVLW 0x78", so that the clock is running fast and then add NOPs to slow it down again.

The one second counter has an additional routine. This reads port A and checks the state of the switches in turn. If the minutes switch is pressed, it branches directly to update the minutes. This means that if the minutes button is held in the pressed position, the minutes will increment at a rate of 1 minute every second. Similarly, the hours switch increments at a rate of one hour every second. **Listing 7.8** refers.

Enhancements

As designed, the clock is powered from a 12V unregulated mains adaptor. If this power fails, the time will be lost. A dry battery can be fitted so that it continues to power the unit during the times when mains derived power is not present.

However, because of the large amount of power taken by the 7 segment display chips, it is recommended that the battery is only used to drive the PIC. This means that the clock will continue to keep the correct time but it will not provide a display until the mains derived power is restored.

References

- PICmicro Mid-Range MCU Family Reference Manual (DS33023A) from www.microchip.com
- 16F8X Reference Manual (DS30430C) from www.microchip.com
- 16F84 Memory Programming Spec (DS30262E) from www.microchip.com
- Application Note AN556 (*Implementing a Table Read*) from www.microchip.com

> **Full Listings**
>
> The complete program listing for this project can be found in the Appendix, and (together with other useful material). at www.rsgb.org/books /extra/picbasics.htm

8

Project 2 - Morse key

Bug keys, of various types, have been with us for an extremely long time now. If you use CW then you either hate them entirely or you have your own favourite type. This key can be configured either as a straightforward bug key or as an Iambic key. It can also be built with one paddle or modified for two paddles or even for no paddles.

With an electronic bug key, when the paddle is pressed to the left it produces a continuous stream of dots. To the right it produces dashes. Even if the paddle is moved from the right to the left halfway through a dash, it will complete that dash and the space that comes after it before sending any dots. If the paddle is released it will complete the dot or dash before stopping.

A single paddle Iambic key produces alternative dots and dashes, starting with a dot if the paddle is moved to the left or starting with a dash if the paddle is moved to the right.

This key has a single paddle and it can be switched between Bug and Iambic modes. It also has the choice of an open collector transistor driver, which is ideal for a modern transceiver, and a relay for higher voltage valve based systems.

Principles of operation

The PIC is clocked from a resistor/capacitor (RC) based oscillator. Although this will drift if frequency over time and when the temperature changes, it allows the frequency to be changed easily, simply by using a potentiometer as part of the resistor element.

The paddle is grounded and pressing it to the left or right puts zero volts onto bit 3 or bit 4 of Port B on the PIC. These bits are otherwise held at a logic one condition by pull up resistors. Switching between bug and Iambic modes is done in a similar manner except that it uses a slide switch that is connected to bit 1 of Port A.

In the PIC's software it first looks at these switches to determine the mode and whether to generate a dot or dash. If the paddle is pressed to either side it generates the key down signal and enters a software loop. For a dot, the key down signal is removed at the end on one loop but the loop executes three times for a dash. Once the key down signal is removed, the loop executes once more before the software looks again at the switches. If the paddle is still depressed in the same direction, the software looks at the slide switch to determine whether to send the same or a different element.

The key down signal comes from bit 4 of Port A, via a 5.6kΩ resistor to the base of an NPN transistor. The emitter is grounded and the collector can be switched either to drive the transceiver directly or to drive a reed relay.

Hardware

I built this into a small aluminium box that had lain unused for years but construction is really a matter of taste. The circuit was built on a small piece of stripboard whilst the paddle was mounted on a piece of copper clad board that had been cut to provide insulation between it and the dot and dash contacts.

Depending on the construction method used, and the amount of RF that is in the area that the key is being used in, some additional decoupling capacitors may be necessary.

Notes on components

Very few of the components are critical. Resistors R1, R2 and R4 are simply pull up resistors and can be any value from 470Ω to 22kΩ. Resistor R3 and the

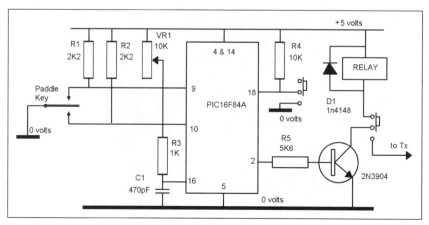

Fig 8.1: Circuit diagram. (Note. 5 volt regulator not shown)

potentiometer form a timing circuit with C1. If the value of C1 is
doubled then the value of the
resistor chain should be halved
and so on. If the resistor chain has
too low a resistance, the oscillator
will stop. That is why the fixed
resistor is in series with the potentiometer. It stops the user from
turning making the resistance too
low.

Depending on the construction
method used, and the amount of
RF that is in the area that the key
is being used in, some additional
10nF decoupling capacitors may
be necessary.

Component List	
IC1	L7805CV (Not shown on circuit diagram)
IC2	PIC 16F84A
C1	470pF
R1, R2	2.2kΩ
R3	1kΩ
R4	10kΩ
R5	5.6kΩ
VR1	10kΩ linear
S1, S2	Slide switches
Misc.	18 pin IC holder
	Wire
	Pins (Optional)
	Paddle and paddle contacts

Component and board layouts

Because of the simplicity of the circuit and the wide variety of personal prefer-
ences for Morse Keys, I have not provided any layout for this project. The internal layout of my own key can be seen from the photograph.

Programming the PIC

Before use, the PIC will need to be programmed. The process for compiling PIC
programs and for programming PIC chips is described elsewhere in this book.

For this project, the configuration bits must be set for an RC oscillator. Both
the watchdog timer and power-up timer must be disabled.

Software operation

Note that anything that comes on a line that is after a semi-colon is a comment
and does not affect the program in any way.

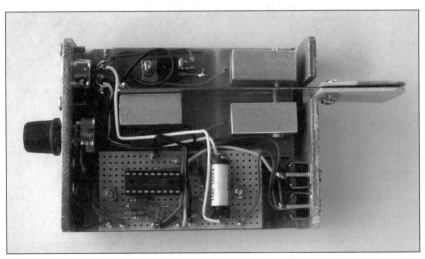

```
#DEFINE   REGHI     BSF 3,5
#DEFINE   REGLO     BCF 3,5
#DEFINE   KEYDN     BSF 5,3
#DEFINE   KEYUP     BCF 5,3


PORTA     EQU       0x05
PORTB     EQU       0x06


W         EQU       0
F         EQU       1


TIMER1    EQU       0x10
TIMER2    EQU       0x11


IAMBIC    EQU       1
DASHKEY   EQU       3
DOTKEY    EQU       4
KEYOUT    EQU       3
```

Listing 8.1: Defining registers

The source code starts by defining some statements and by declaring some registers and bits (**Listing 8.1**). This simply makes the source code easier to read. For example, by defining 'bsf 5,3' as 'KEYDN', the word keydn (key down) can be used rather than an impersonal call on a certain bit of a certain register.

The next stage is to initialise the registers. On Port A, bits 0 and 1 are set to inputs whilst bits 2, 3 and 4 are set to outputs. All of the bits on Port B are set to inputs. **Listing 8.2** refers.

Then follows the loop where the program waits for the paddle to be moved (**Listing 8.3**). This loop uses bit test instructions to test for the relevant paddle movement. If the paddle is moved it goes to the dot or dash routines. Both routines are similar so **Listing 8.4** shows only the dash routine.

```
          REGHI
          MOVLW     0x03          ;Set PORTA bits 0,1 to outputs,
          MOVWF     PORTA         ;bits 2,3,4 to inputs
          MOVLW     0xFF
          MOVWF     PORTB         ;Set PORTB to all outputs
          REGLO
```

Listing 8.2: Initialisation

```
LOOP    BTFSS     PORTB, DOTKEY   ;Is Dot Key Pressed
        GOTO      DOT             ;Yes, go to Dot routine
        BTFSS     PORTB, DASHKEY  ;Is Dash Key Pressed
        GOTO      DASH            ;Yes, go to Dash routine
        GOTO      LOOP
```

Listing 8.3: Initial loop

```
DASH    KEYDN
        NOP
        NOP
        NOP
        NOP
        NOP
        NOP
        CALL      TIME
        CALL      TIME
        CALL      TIME
        KEYUP
        CALL      TIME
        BTFSC     PORTB, DASHKEY   ;Is Dash Key Still pressed?
        GOTO      LOOP             ;No, so go back to loop
        BTFSS     PORTA, IAMBIC    ;Yes - Is Iambic switch set?
        GOTO      DASH             ;No so do another Dash
        GOTO      DOT              ;Yes, so do a dot
```

Listing 8.4: Dash routine   When the key was tested, it didn't sound right so a number of NOP instructions were added to balance the key down to key up ratio. These routines generate a key down signal before calling a subroutine called "time". The dot routine calls this only once but the dash routine calls this three times. It then lifts the key and calls the time subroutine again. Then it checks whether the key is still in the same condition. If it is and the Iambic/bug switch is set in the bug condition, it will repeat the same routine. If the switch is in the Iambic position, it will jump to the other routine.

The time routine is simply two nested software loops. The inner loop runs 128 times and the outer loop 22 times.

Options and enhancements

Timing

If the key is too fast, even with the speed turned to maximum resistance, increase the value of the capacitor C1. Conversely, if it is too slow, with the speed turned to minimum resistance, decrease the capacitor. Alternately, change the timing loop. To speed up the key, change the line "TIME MOVLW 0x16" to a lower value. A higher value will slow down the key.

Listing 8.5: Delay loop

```
TIME    MOVLW     0x16             ;16 hex is 22 decimal
        MOVWF     TIMER1
T1      MOVLW     0x80             ;80 hex is 128 decimal
        MOVWF     TIMER2
T2      DECFSZ    TIMER2, F
        GOTO      T2
        DECFSZ    TIMER1, F
        GOTO      T1
        RETURN
```

Two paddle key

Some CW operators prefer a key with two paddles. In this case, it is often easier to make the keys open a circuit when they are operated rather than make a circuit. Simply change the 'BTFSS PORTB' instructions to 'BTFSC PORTB' in the line with the label of LOOP and two lines after that. Then change the 'BTFSC PORTB' instructions to 'BTFSS PORTB' in the third line from the end of the DOT and DASH routines.

(Do not change the lines that say 'BTFSS PORTA' in the DOT and DASH routines.)

Squeeze key

This is another variant on the two paddle key. If the right paddle is pressed, the key sends dots. The left paddle sends dashes. Pressing both keys together will send alternate dots and dashes. To achieve this, simply change the lines that say 'BTFSS PORTA, IAMBIC' to:

- BTFSC   PORTA, DOTKEY   in the DASH routine, and
- BTFSC   PORTA, DASHKEY   in the DOT routine.

(This assumes that the key makes contacts to generate CW. If the key opens contact to send CW, change the BTFSC to BTFSS.)

The no paddle key

As an alternative to paddles, touch pads can be used. Simply place a finger across the pads and it will trigger the key. The following circuit shows a dot or dash circuit for a bug or for an Iambic keyer.

Adjust the preset potentiometer for a high signal to the PIC when the pads are touched and a low when the finger is removed. (See section on two paddle keys for details on how to change the software for an active high paddle). Pads can be made from any conductive material, such as copper clad board or even round headed screws.

Full Listings
The complete program listing for this project can be found in the Appendix, and (together with other useful material) at www.rsgb.org/books /extra/picbasics.htm

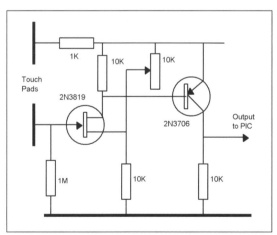

Components List	
TR1	NJFet 2N3819
TR2	PNP transistor 2N3906
R1	1MΩ
R2	1kΩ
R3, R4, R5	10kΩ
VR1	10kΩ linear potentiometer

Fig 8.2: No paddle key

References

- PICmicro Mid-Range MCU Family Reference Manual (DS33023A) from www.microchip.com
- 16F8X Reference Manual (DS30430C) from www.microchip.com
- 16F84 Memory Programming Specification (DS30262E) from

www.microchip.com
- Homebrew your Iambic Keyer (*QST* Feb 2005, page 40)
- Smart Keyer Lite (*QST* May 2004, 42)
- Uncle Albert's Touch Pad Keyer (*QST* Oct 2001, page 32)
- Bugambic (*RadCom* April 2002, page 29)

9

Project 3 - Automatic Morse generator

I n contests, a lot of time is spent repetitively calling CQ. This little unit sits between the key and the transceiver. Either a straight key or an electronic key could be used. Press one button and it will send a complete message. What's more, because PIC chips are so easy to program, the message can be changed for each contest if you want to.

Principles of operation

Before the contest, the program needs to be is written. This can be done manually or there is a PC program available that will allow a plain text message to be typed in. This program is then compiled and loaded into the PIC.

Like the Morse Key, which it is based on, the Automatic Morse Generator uses a variable RC oscillator. This allows the speed of the generated Morse code to be varied.

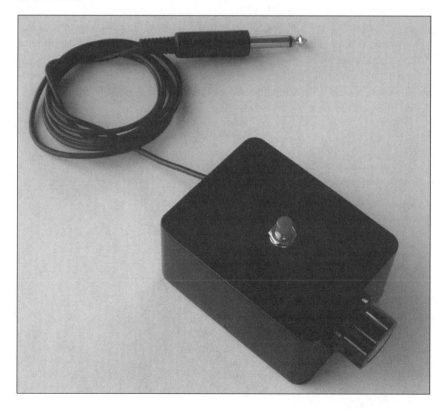

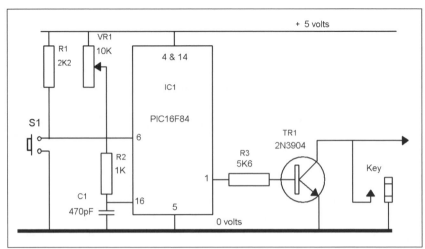

Fig 9.1: Circuit diagram

Once the button has been pressed, the program reads the first item from a list of Morse commands. This tells the program to call a dot, dash, intercharacter space or a long inter-word space routine. The dot and dash routines activate the key, dot for one time period and a dash for three time periods. Both routines then release the key for a time period. The space and long space deactivate the key for four or six time periods. Then the program reads the next item from the list.

Hardware

My unit was built in to a small plastic box with a potentiometer to control the speed, a button to start the message, sockets for power and the key into plus a cable with a jack plug on the end. I derived my power from the same supply that powers the transceiver.

I did not include a relay as my transceivers have less than 12 volts on the key socket. However, one could be added if necessary. See Morse Key project for details.

Component List	
IC1	L7805CV (Not shown on circuit diagram)
IC2	PIC 16F84A
TR1	NPN transistor 2N3904
C1	470pF
R1	2.2kΩ
R2	1kΩ
R3	5.6kΩ
VR1	10kΩ linear potentiometer
S1	Push Button Switch
Misc.	18 pin IC holder
	Socket for Morse Key
	Wire
	Pins (Optional)
	Paddle and paddle contacts

Notes on components

Very few of the components are critical. R1 is simply a pull up resistor and can be any value from 470Ω to 22kΩ. R2 and the potentiometer form a timing circuit with C1. If the value of C1 is doubled then the value of the resistor chain should be halved and so on. If the resistor chain has too low a resistance, the oscillator will stop. The fixed resistor R2 in series with the potentiomete stops the user from setting the resistance too low.

Depending on the construction method used, and the amount of RF that is in the area that the key is being used in, some additional 10nF decoupling capacitors may be necessary.

Programming the PIC

Before use, the PIC will need to be programmed. The process for compiling PIC programs and for programming PIC chips is described elsewhere in this book.

For this project, the configuration bits must be set for an RC oscillator. Both the watchdog timer and power-up timer must be disabled.

Software operation

Note that anyting that comes on a line after a semi-colon is a comment and does not affect the program in any way.

The source code starts by defining some statements and by declaring some registers and bits (**Listing 9.1**). This simply makes the source code easier to read.

For example, by defining 'bsf 5,1' as 'KEYDN', the word keydn (key down) can be used rather than an impersonal call on a certain bit of a certain register.

The next stage is to initialise the registers. Port A is set to all outputs whilst Port B is set to all inputs. However, only one bit is used on each of these ports. See **Listing 9.2**.

```
#DEFINE   REGHI    BSF 3,5
#DEFINE   REGLO    BCF 3,5
#DEFINE   KEYDN    BSF 5,1
#DEFINE   KEYUP    BCF 5,1
PCL       EQU      0x02
PORTA     EQU      0x05
PORTB     EQU      0x06
PCLATH    EQU      0x0A
W         EQU      0
F         EQU      1
OFFSET    EQU      0x0D
TIMER1    EQU      0x10
TIMER2    EQU      0x11
KEYOUT    EQU      1
```

Listing 9.1: Assigning the registers

```
CLRF     PORTA
CLRF     PORTB
CLRF     PCLATH
REGHI
CLRF     PORTA        ;Set PORTA to all outputs
MOVLW    0xFF
MOVLW    PORTB        ;Set PORTB to all inputs
REGLO
```

Listing 9.2: Initialising the registers

```
LOOP    BTFSS   PORTB,0      ;Is the switch pressed
        GOTO    XTABLE       ;Yes
        GOTO    LOOP         ;No
```

Listing 9.3: Wait routine

This is followed by a loop that simply waits for the button to be pressed (**Listing 9.3**).

Once the button is pressed, it jumps to a list of dot/dash/space commands (**Listing 9.4**). This table is configured for the message to be sent. The following table sends the letters 'CQ' followed by an inter-word space. It then returns to the loop that waits for the button to be pressed again.

(Note that the word TABLE or any word starting with TABLE is reserved in MPASM and must not be used in a program. It can, however, be used with TASM)

The dash and space routines are shown in **Listing 9.5**. Dot is similar to dash except that it only calls 'TIME' once between the KEYDN and KEYUP instructions.

Long is similar to space except that it calls 'TIME' five times.

(Note that the word SPACE is also a reserved in MPASM and must not be used in a program. It can, however, be used with TASM)

The time routine is simply two nested software loops (**Listing 9.6**). The inner loop runs 128 times and the outer loop 22 times.

```
XTABLE  CALL    DASH
        CALL    DOT
        CALL    DASH
        CALL    DOT
        CALL    XSPACE
        CALL    DASH
        CALL    DASH
        CALL    DOT
        CALL    DASH
        CALL    LONG
        GOTO    LOOP
```

Listing 9.4: Morse message

```
DASH      KEYDN
          CALL      TIME
          CALL      TIME
          CALL      TIME
          KEYUP
          CALL      TIME
          RETURN



XSPACE    CALL      TIME
          CALL      TIME
          CALL      TIME
          RETURN
```

Listing 9.5: Dash routine

```
TIME      MOVLW     0x16            ;16 hex is 22 decimal
          MOVWF     TIMER1
T1        MOVLW     0x80            ;80 hex is 128 decimal
          MOVWF     TIMER2
T2        DECFSZ    TIMER2,F
          GOTO      T2
          DECFSZ    TIMER1,F
          GOTO      T1
          RETURN
```

Configuring the generator

Listing 9.6: Delay routine

The generator can be configured in one of two distinct ways:

- By manually configuring the table. Instructions are executed from the top to the bottom. Please remember to add a 'GOTO LOOP' at the end if you want the generator to stop. You can loop the generator by changing this to 'GOTO TABLE' but note that this generator has no break-in facilities.

- By running a program called MORSE.EXE. This program runs under DOS or Windows. It will ask for an assembler filename to create. Then it will ask for your character string. This can be in upper case (capitals) or lower case. Special Morse characters can also be included. The program will combine your string with a file called 'BASE.PIC' to produce a complete assembler file that is ready to compile.

Note:
MORSE.EXE can be downloaded from www.rsgb.org/books /extra/picbasics.htm

The maximum message length is about 1900 dots/dashes/spaces. This equates to about 200 characters.

The maximum size of the code and the characters must not exceed 2047 instructions.

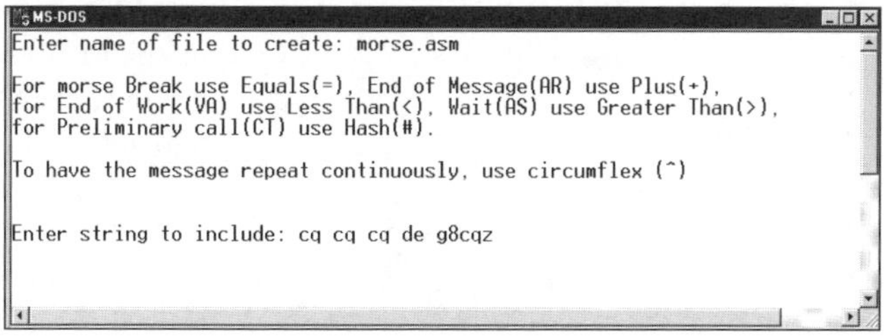

```
MS-DOS
Enter name of file to create: morse.asm

For morse Break use Equals(=), End of Message(AR) use Plus(+),
for End of Work(VA) use Less Than(<), Wait(AS) use Greater Than(>),
for Preliminary call(CT) use Hash(#).

To have the message repeat continuously, use circumflex (^)

Enter string to include: cq cq cq de g8cqz
```

Fig 9.2: Screen capture from the morse.exe program

Fig 9.3: Break in keyer

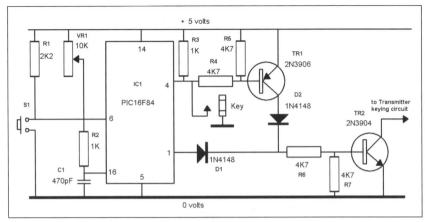

Options and enhancements

Timing

If the key is too fast, even with the speed turned to maximum resistance, increase the value of the capacitor C1. Conversely, if it is too slow, with the speed turned to minimum resistance, decrease the capacitor.

Alternatively, change the timing loop. To speed up the key, change the line 'TIME MOVLW 0x16' to a lower value. A higher value will slow down the key.

Break-in

One of the most useful options is to be able to break-in to a message that the generator is sending. This can be done by moving the key from being in parallel with the output and adding an extra transistor stage (see **Fig 9.3**). Note that a diode is now placed in series with pin 1 of the PIC and that pin 4 no longer goes directly to the 5 volt line.

If the external key is up, the 1kΩ resistor will pull pin 4 of the PIC to a logic one condition and the PIC runs normally. The PNP 2N3906 has no voltage between its base and emitter so it passes no current. If the PIC puts a positive voltage on pin 1, the diode conducts and switches the 2N3904 on, closing the key circuit to the transceiver. For a zero voltage output on pin 1, the 2N3904 is switched off because of the 4.7kΩ resistor between its base and emitter.

When the external key is pressed, pin 4 of the PIC goes low. As this is the master reset pin, the PIC resets itself and pin 1 goes low. Even when this signal is removed, the PIC will wait for the button to be pressed before sending the message again.

Anyway, the low signal on pin 4 turns on the 2N3906. This in turn

Components List	
IC1	PIC16F84
TR1	PNP transistor 2N3906
TR2	NPN transistor 2N3904
D1, D2	Diode 1N4148
C1	470pF
R1	2.2kΩ
R2, R3	1kΩ
R4, R5, R6, R7	4.7kΩ
VR1	10kΩ linear potentiometer
S1	Push to Make switch

switches the diode on and this switches the 2N3904 on. The result is that all key depressions are transferred directly through to the output.

Multiple messages

With the above circuits, only bit zero of Port B is being used. However, there is no reason why the other bits of port B cannot be used, giving a choice of up to 8 messages. For example, switch 1 could be a CQ, switch 2 could be a QRZ message etc.

An 8 message generator can be achieved by connecting each Port B pin of the 16F84, from pin 6 to pin 13, to a pull-up resistor and a push switch that lowers the pin to zero volts when it is pushed (**Fig 9.4**).

In the PIC, the software will need to be modified by creating a separate table for each message. Open the file called BASEMUL-TI.PIC. Configure messages 'XTABLE2' to 'XTABLE8'. Save the file as BASE.PIC, being careful not to overwrite any other file with this name. Then, use the PC program to configure message 1. The

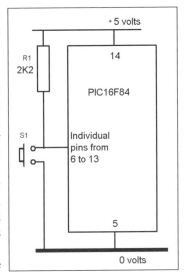

Fig 9.4: Multiple message generator circuit diagram

Photo 9.2: Multi message generator

Photo 9.3: Internal view

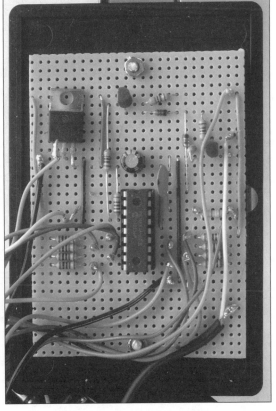

```
LOOP    BTFSS       PORTB,0             ;Is Switch 1 pressed
        GOTO        XTABLE              ;Yes
        BTFSS       PORTB,1             ;Is Switch 2 pressed
        GOTO        XTABLE1             ;Yes
        BTFSS       PORTB,2             ;Is Switch 3 pressed
        GOTO        XTABLE2             ;Yes
        BTFSS       PORTB,3             ;Is Switch 4 pressed
        GOTO        XTABLE3             ;Yes
        BTFSS       PORTB,4             ;Is Switch 5 pressed
        GOTO        XTABLE4             ;Yes
        BTFSS       PORTB,5             ;Is Switch 6 pressed
        GOTO        XTABLE5             ;Yes
        BTFSS       PORTB,6             ;Is Switch 7 pressed
        GOTO        XTABLE6             ;Yes
        BTFSS       PORTB,7             ;Is Switch 8 pressed
        GOTO        XTABLE7             ;Yes
        GOTO        LOOP                ;No switches pressed
```

Listing 9.7: Switch routine

reason for this is that, in my experience, only one message needs to be changed regularly. By calling that message 'XTABLE', I can use the PC program to generate it from plain text.

(Note that the word TABLE is a reserved word in MPASM, therefore it is preceded by the letter X).

Within the base PIC software, the loop is expanded to look at each switch in turn (**Listing 9.7**)

In-circuit programming

Because of the potential need to reprogram this PIC before every contest, this project lends itself to in-circuit programming.

To put the PIC into programming mode, the master clear pin (pin 4) must be raised to 12-14 volts. In order to avoid this damaging the key, two additional diodes are needed (**Fig 9.5**). In addition, the external key must be removed. I use an adapter that plugs in to the key socket and applies the programming voltage. This prevents any chance of damaging the key during reprogramming. The actual programming signals are then applied to pins 12 (clock or strobe) and 13 (data).

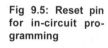

Fig 9.5: Reset pin for in-circuit programming

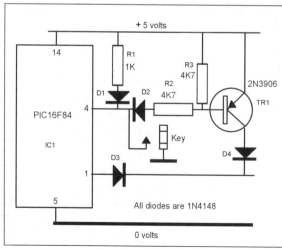

Full Listings

The complete program listing for this project can be found in the Appendix, and (together with other useful material) at www.rsgb.org/books /extra/picbasics.htm

This has been done by bringing these signals out to a small socket on the case.

References

- PICmicro Mid-Range MCU Family Reference Manual (DS33023A) from www.microchip.com
- 16F8X Reference Manual (DS30430C) from www.microchip.com
- 16F84 Memory Programming Specification (DS30262E) from www.microchip.com

10

Project 4 - Two-tone audio generator

T he use of a two tone audio generator where the tones are not harmonically related is recommended to align SSB transmitters. This PIC based audio generator can generate a variety of waveforms including two tone waveforms. However, it should be noted that not every frequency can be generated by this design.

Principles of operation

Like all Digital to Analogue converters, this generator outputs a digital signal that is converted into an analogue voltage. This is achieved by a resistor ladder attached to port B. By sample-switching this signal, and therefore the analogue voltage, an approximation of an audio waveform can be generated. This waveform will have the switching frequency imposed upon it and this needs to be removed if a clean signal is needed. Therefore, the switching frequency is important and it should be as high as possible so that it is easier to remove.

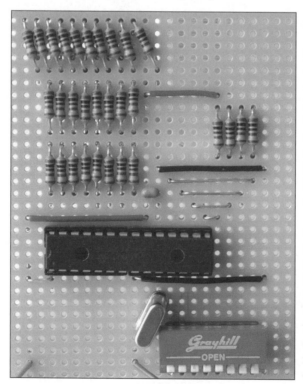

For this project, a switching speed of 12kHz was used. This is not as high as I would have liked but it was a compromise between having long waveform descriptions and having higher quality audio. Even so, it is a higher switching frequency than the audio recorder uses.

In order to provide several different frequencies, the PIC reads a DIL switch-bank that is connected to port C. In this application, only bits 5 to 7 are used but this could easily be extended to produce more than seven different tones.

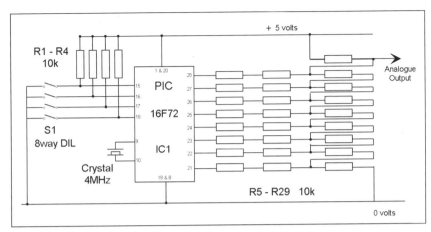

Fig 10.1: Circuit diagram

	Component List
IC1	PIC 16F72 (or 16F73 or 16F872 or 16F873)
R1 - R29	10kΩ
Crystal	4MHz
S1	8-way DIL switch in a 16 pin socket
Misc	2 x 14 pin IC socket or 28 pin x 0.3" socket
	Wire

Hardware

The resistor ladder was built from 10kΩ resistors, using two in series where 20kΩ is required. A 4MHz crystal is used to provide the timing.

Notes on components

- A 16F84 can be used if the board layout is changed and the software reads the switches from port A instead of from port C.
- R1 - R29 must all be the same value.

Designing the waveforms

My first design stage was the waveforms. The frequency must be a whole sub-multiple of 12kHz. Divide 12kHz by the desired frequency. If the result is not a whole number, multiply it by a whole number (integer) until it is. If the result is less than 252 then the waveform can be generated. Otherwise it cannot. For example:

- 1kHz is 1/12 of 12kHz
- 2.5kHz is not directly divisible into 12kHz (12/2.5=4.8) but 4.8 times 5 is 24 and 24 is less than 252.
- 2.7kHz is not directly divisible into 12kHz (12/2.7=4.4) but 4.4 times 27 is 100
- 3.33kHz is not directly divisible into 12kHz or any or its harmonics up to 333. (333 times 3.33kHz is 100 times 12kHz) but 333 is longer than a PIC table can easily be made so this frequency cannot be generated. However, 3.3kHz can be. 12 divided by 3.3 times 33 is a whole number (100).

111

The final whole number is the number of steps that the PIC will make to generate the waveform and the number of times that you had to multiply the initial division to get it is the number of cycles that these steps will generate. So, to generate 2.7kHz will require the PIC to generate 100 steps and in doing so, it will generate 27 cycles.

For a sine wave, take the result of the first division (12 divided by 2.7 in this example) and divide this into 360 degrees to get the angle of each step (exactly 81° in this example). Now get the sine of 81° (0.9876883405951). A sine can range in value from plus one to minus one. Multiply by 127 and add 128. The result is a number in the range of 1 to 255. (Minus one times 127 is -127, plus 128 is one. Plus one times 127 is 127 plus 128 is 255). Round all numbers down, so 81° gives a number of 253 (or 0xFD in hexadecimal). Add the angle and repeat, so 81° plus 81° is 162° and the sine of 162° (times 127 plus 128) is 0xA7. Continue repeating for the required number of steps.

For a two tone signal, find a number of steps that is common to both frequencies.

For example, 800Hz and 1.5kHz will both generate with 120 steps. In that time, 800Hz will generate 15 cycles and 1.5kHz will generate 8 cycles. Find the sines as before but multiply each by 64 and add them together before adding 128 to the total.

Other waveform shapes can be generated by changing the mathematics. For a saw-tooth, divide 360 by the result of that first division to get the step size. Then divide 255 by the step size to get the value. For example, to generate 2.7kHz as a saw-tooth, divide 12 by 2.7 (4.444) then divide 255 by 4.444 to get the value (57 or 0x39). For the next step, add the value again. If the result is more than 255, subtract 255 and keep going.

Programming the PIC

Before use, the PIC will need to be programmed. The process for compiling PIC programs and for programming PIC chips is described elsewhere in this book.

For this project, the configuration bits must be set for a high speed crystal oscillator. Both the watchdog timer and power-up timer must be disabled. If a 16F872 or 16F873 PIC is being used, low voltage programming must also be disabled.

Software operation

Listing 10.1: Declaring the registers
Apart from the program counter and the ports, only two user registers are declared - see **Listing 10.1**.

```
PCL      EQU      0x02        ;Program counter low byte
PORTB    EQU      0x06        ;Output to Digital to Analogue
PORTC    EQU      0x07        ;Input from Switches
PCLATH   EQU      0x0A        ;Program Counter high byte
TIMER    EQU      0x21        ;User register for timing
STEP     EQU      0x22        ;Waveform step number
W        EQU      0
F        EQU      1
```

```
START   BSF     3, 5        ;Go to register bank 1
        CLRF    PORTB       ;Make port B all outputs
        MOVLW   0xFF        ;Make port C all inputs
        MOVWF   PORTC
        BCF     3, 5        ;Go back to register bank zero
        MOVLW   0x01        ;Select waveform step 1
        MOVWF   STEP
```

Listing 10.2: Initialising the registers

```
LOOP    CLRF    PCLATH      ;Set high program counter to zero
        SWAPF   PORTC, W    ;Read switches
        ANDLW   0x07        ;Get switches 4-6
        ADDWF   PCL, F      ;Add switch number to program counter
        GOTO    T0          ;Tone 0 = No Tone
        GOTO    T1          ;Tone 1 = 800Hz
        GOTO    T2          ;Tone 2 = 1500Hz
        GOTO    T3          ;Tone 3 = Two Tone (800+1500)
        GOTO    T5          ;Tone 4 = 1kHz
        GOTO    T5          ;Tone 5 = 300Hz
        GOTO    T6          ;Tone 6 = 2.7kHz
        GOTO    T7          ;Tone 7 = 3.3kHz
```

Listing 10.3: Switch selection

The ports are initialised so that port B is an output and port C is an input (**Listing 10.2**).

The program then enters its main loop and looks at the switches (**Listing 10.3**). A table read is used to decide which of the waveform routines to go to. Note that, in this example, switches on bits 4 to 6 of port C are used and that one of the tones is a 'no signal' tone.

To set the 'no signal' tone, port B is set to a value of 128 (**Listing 10.4**). This is exactly half of the available output voltage.

For the other signals, another table read is used: (Tone 2 shown in **Listing 10.5**))

```
T0      MOVLW   0x80        ;No Tone
        MOVWF   PORTB       ;Move 0x80 (128) to port B
        CT0     MOVLW   0x80 ;No Tone
        MOVWF   PORTB       ;Move 0x80 (128) to port B
        CALL    DELAY       ;Wait
        CALL    DELAY       ;Wait a bit longer
        GOTO    LOOP        ;Read switches again
ALL     DELAY   ;Wait
        CALL    DELAY       ;Wait a bit longer
        GOTO    LOOP        ;Read switches again
```

Listing 10.4: No tone

```
T2      MOVLW    0x00            ;1500kHz Tone
        MOVWF    PCLATH          ;Set high program counter
        MOVLW    0x08            ;Prepare in case end of cycle
        DECFSZ   STEP, F         ;Next step (end of cycle)
        GOTO     J2              ;No
        MOVWF    STEP            ;Yes so reload step count
J2      CALL     DELAY           ;Delay for 12kHz
        CALL     TA2             ;Call table read
        MOVWF    PORTB           ;Move data to output
        GOTO     LOOP            ;Read switches again

        ORG      0x80            ;Set memory storage area
TA2     MOVF     STEP, W         ;Get step number
        ADDWF    PCL, F          ;Add to program counter
        RETLW    0x00            ;Return with data
        RETLW    0x80
        RETLW    0xDA
        RETLW    0xFF
        RETLW    0xDA
        RETLW    0x80
        RETLW    0x25
        RETLW    0x00
        RETLW    0x25
```

Listing 10.5: Tone 2

```
DELAY   MOVLW    0x11            ;0x11 = 17
        MOVWF    TIMER
D1      DECFSZ   TIMER, F        ;17 x 3 = 51uS
        GOTO     D1
        NOP                      ;Trimmer NOPs
        NOP
        RETURN
```

Listing 10.6: Delay routine

Full Listings

The complete program listing for this project can be found in the Appendix, and (together with other useful material) at www.rsgb.org/books /extra/picbasics.htm

Note that the table must fall entirely within a 256 instruction area. To ensure that this happens, it may be necessary to use an ORG command. This command tells the compiler where to place the routine.

Where the routine is placed beyond the first 0x100 instructions, PCLATH must be set. For example, if the table is prefixed by ORG 0x400, PCLATH must be loaded with 0x04.

A common delay routine is used. This simply extends the time to allow samples to be output at a rate of 12kHz. The routine itself comprises a tight loop plus some NOP instructions.

References

- PICmicro Mid-Range MCU Family Reference Manual (DS33023A) from www.microchip.com
- 16F87X Reference Manual (DS30292C) from www.microchip.com
- 16F87XA Flash Memory Programming Specification (DS35889B) from www.microchip.com
- Application Note AN556 (Implementing a Table Read) from www.microchip.com

11

Project 5 - 30MHz frequency counter

T here are many PIC based counter designs but most are based on doing 'clever' things with the prescaler so as to minimise the chip count. I have taken a slightly different approach and the result is a reliable design that is simple to understand and build.

General purpose frequency counters are a compromise between speed and precision. For example, a counter that measures in hertz can only take one measurement each second. This is great for taking accurate frequency measurements but it makes rough alignment difficult.

Measurements in kilohertz can be taken in a millisecond and this gives a smooth flow of readings that makes it easy to make rough alignments. For this counter, I decided to have a precision of 10Hz. This is sufficient precision for most Amateur Radio projects whilst giving a relatively smooth flow of readings.

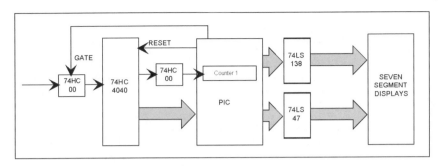

Fig 11.1: Block diagram

Principles of operation

I designed this counter to have a maximum count of 50MHz although I have only tested it to 30MHz over any real period of time.

To take a reading of 50MHz in 10Hz steps means that the counter must be capable of reading up to 5 million steps. In binary, this is 10011000100101101000000 or 23 bits (23 ones and zeros). If all those bits are set, as they would be at an absolute maximum count, the reading would be 8,388,607 or some 83MHz.

However, no PIC has a 23 bit counter in it. The maximum resolution is 16 bits plus an inaccessible 8 bit prescaler. Whilst some designs work by 'topping up' the prescaler until it overflows, I decided to use an additional and fully accessible 74HC4040 counter chip to provide the additional 7 bits. Actually, it was easier to use 8 bits rather than 7. Because this external counter goes in front of the PIC's own counter, it was necessary to provide a gate on the input.

The basic process to take a count is:

- Reset the external counter
- Reset the internal counter
- Open the gate
- Wait for 100mS whilst maintaining display
- Close the gate
- Read the external counter
- Convert the reading from binary to decimal digits
- Output to display.

The necessity to maintain the display whilst the gate is open should be noted. This project uses seven-segment displays and these require multiplexing every 1ms or so for them to provide a display that does not flicker. Seven digits are used in this design.

This design works well with a digital (TTL) input, but an amplifier is needed to measure smaller analogue signals.

Hardware

The design and layout for the seven segment displays is given elsewhere in this book.

The Amplifier

The design for this amplifier came from the commercial UniCounter (a single digit frequency counter). My unit was built 'dead bug' style on a piece of single sided copper-clad board as a ground plane. Holes were drilled, then the body of

Component List	
TR1	NJFET 2N3819 (or any N channel JFET with a frequency rating of 100MHz or more)
TR2	NPN transistor 2N3904 (or 2N2369 or a similar NPN transistor)
R1	100kΩ (or up to 470kΩ)
R2, R4	470Ω
R3	68kΩ (select for about 2.5 volts on collector of TR2)
C1	33pF (or up to 100pF)
C2, C3	22nF (10nF to 100nF)

Fig 11.2: Amplifier circuit

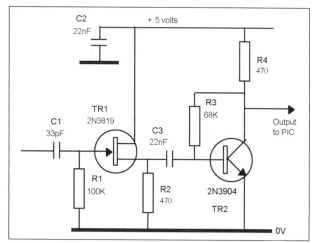

each transistor was glued into the hole with its legs standing up away from the board. Then, using a file or cutter on a hobby drill, islands were cut for the drain of the 2N3819 and the collector of the 2N3904. As an alternative, small pieces of copper clad board can be glued on top of the main board to provide islands for the positive line and for the collector of the 2N3904. Other components are soldered directly together or to the ground plane.

Note that the output is directly coupled to the input gate via a short length of screened cable. There is no blocking capacitor.

Amplifier board

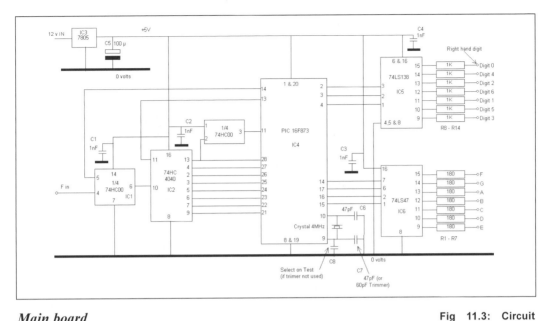

Main board

The input signal goes to one of the four AND gates that make up the 74HC00 chip. The other input to that AND gate comes from bit 3 of port C on the PIC and this is used to open the gate for the specified time period.

The output from the 74HC00 gate goes in to the 74HC4040. This is a 12 stage counter, although in this application only 8 stages are used. Note that the 74HC00 and the 74HC4040 are mounted different ways round on the board. The reset pin of the 74HC4040 comes from bit 2 of port C on the PIC and this is used to clear the count between readings. Two outputs are taken from the counter chip. A par-

Main board

allel output is passed to port B of the PIC. Note the way that bit numbers 5 to 7 are not in the same order on both chips so there is a need to carefully connect these. There is also a problem with the serial connection. 74HC4040 chips increment their count on the negative going edge of their inputs but the PIC counters increment on the positive going edge. During the design phase, this gave some very interesting effects, as a gradually increasing frequency seemed to jump up and down in frequency. This problem was overcome by passing the signal back through one of the 74HC00 gates that was wired to act as an inverter, before taking it to counter 1 of the PIC via the bit 0 pin of port C.

For the output to the display, port A is used to drive a 74LS138, which enables the digits in turn. Binary inputs to this chip are taken from port A on the PIC but, because the bit numbers supplied to the chip are different to those listed in the 74LS138 datasheet, the output pins are not sequential. Some care may be needed when connecting up the display to ensure that the digits are lit in the correct order.

The actual digits are provided via a 73LS47 decoder /driver chip. This requires a four bit binary coded decimal (BCD) number and this is passed via bits 4 to 7 of port C.

Component List	
IC1	74HC00
IC2	74HC4040
IC3	L7805CV
IC4	PIC16F72 (or 16F73 or 16F872 or 16F873)
IC5	74LS138
IC6	74LS47
Crystal	4MHz
R1 - R7	180Ω
R8 - R14	1kΩ
C1, C2, C3, C4	1nF
C5	100µF 16V
C6, C7	47pF (or 60pF trimmers. See text)
C8	Select on test (not required if trimmer is used)

The main board is constructed from a sandwich of stripboard and plain single sided copper clad board.

These are mounted with their insulator sides together. Cutouts in the copper clad board allow the chips to be mounted on the stripboard and holes are drilled as required to make connections from the zero volt lines on the stripboard to the face of the copper clad board.

My counters have used select on test capacitors rather than trimmers but either could be used. I have found that 2pF moved the display by about 10Hz.

Programming the PIC

Before use, the PIC will need to be programmed. The process for compiling PIC programs and for programming PIC chips is described elsewhere in this book.

For this project, the configuration bits must be set for a high speed crystal oscillator, and both the watchdog timer and power-up timer must be disabled.

Software description

The critical part of the program is the timing and there are two critical timings:
- The display needs to be updated every 1ms. The display is on an 8 digit loop even though there are only seven digits. This is because eight is a cyclic binary number (0 to 8 inclusive is exactly three bits).
- The gate needs to be opened for exactly 100ms. This is done by setting a counter to 100 and decrementing it every time the display is updated.

In addition to these loops, there is a need to translate the counts from binary to decimal and this could take a variable amount of time. Therefore, this needs to be undertaken outside of both loops.

If the program concentrates on the 1ms loop then a 100ms loop would finish part way through a cycle of digits and this would create a noticeable blink on the display. Therefore although the gate is closed at the end of 100ms, a process that takes only a couple of microseconds, the display loop continues to the end of that cycle of seven digits before the binary to BCD translation is made during the next millisecond or so.

Then, the cycle starts over with the gate being opened. The result is a flicker free display and an accurate count.

```
        INDR     EQU        0x00              ;Indirect access register
        PCL      EQU        0x02              ;Program counter (used for table
        reads)
        STATUS   EQU        0x03              ;Used for Zero bit
        FSR      EQU        0x04              ;Indirect access address
        PORTA    EQU        0x05              ;Digit output to display
        PORTB    EQU        0x06              ;From external counter
        PORTC    EQU        0x07              ;Counter and display control
        PCLATH   EQU        0x0A              ;Program Counter High Bits
        INTCON   EQU        0x0B              ;Interrupt Control
        TMR1L    EQU        0x0E              ;Least Significant Byte of Counter
        TMR1H    EQU        0x0F              ;Most Significant Byte of Counter
        T1CON    EQU        0x10              ;Counter Control
        D7       EQU        0x20              ;BCD digit 7
        D6       EQU        0x21              ;BCD digit 6
        D5       EQU        0x22              ;BCD digit 5
        D4       EQU        0x23              ;BCD digit 4
        D3       EQU        0x24              ;BCD digit 3
        D2       EQU        0x25              ;BCD digit 2
        D1       EQU        0x26              ;BCD digit 1
        D0       EQU        0x27              ;BCD digit 0
        DIGIT    EQU        0x28              ;Digit number to control display
        CHAR     EQU        0x29              ;Used to build Port C data
        DELAY    EQU        0x2B              ;Part of 1ms loop
        LCOUNT   EQU        0x2C              ;100 - 0ms count in millisecs
        HDATA    EQU        0x32              ;Part of Bin-BCD (Binary Byte)
        HTEMP    EQU        0x33              ;Register used in Bin-BCD conversion
        HCARRY   EQU        0x34              ;Carry bit to next BCD digit
        HOFFSET  EQU        0x35              ;Digit number for Bin-BCD conversion
        HOFFBIT  EQU        0x36              ;Bit number of byte being converted

        W        EQU        0
        F        EQU        1
        CARRY    EQU        0
        ZERO     EQU        2
        TMR1ON   EQU        0
        TMR1CS   EQU        1
        T1SYNC   EQU        2
        T1OSCEN  EQU        3
        T1CKPS0  EQU        4
        T1CKPS1  EQU        5
        GATE     EQU        3                 ;Opens/closes the external gate
        RST      EQU        2                 ;Resets the external counter
```

Listing 11.1: Register and bit declarations

```
BSF      3, 5               ;Go to register bank 1
BCF      3, 6
MOVLW    0x18               ;PORTA = (0-2=Output) (3-4=Input)
CLRF     PORTA
MOVLW    $FF
MOVWF    PORTB              ;PORTB = Input
MOVLW    $03
MOVWF    PORTC              ;PORTC = (0-1=Input) (2-7=Output)
BCF      3, 5               ;Go back to register bank 0
CLRF     PCLATH             ;Clear high bits of program counter
CLRF     DIGIT              ;Clear all BCD digits
CLRF     D0
CLRF     D1
CLRF     D2
CLRF     D3
CLRF     D4
CLRF     D5
CLRF     D6
CLRF     D7
CLRF     T1CON              ;Set Timer 1 to no prescaler or osc
BSF      T1CON, T1OSCEN     ;Enable Timer 1
BSF      T1CON, TMR1CS      ;No timer synchronisation
BCF      PORTC, GATE        ;Close external gate
```

Listing 11.2: Register initialisation

```
LONG    MOVLW    0x64               ;Set ms count to 100
        MOVWF    LCOUNT
        CLRF     DIGIT              ;Reset display to digit 0
        BSF      PORTC, RST         ;Apply reset to external counter
        CLRF     TMR1L              ;Reset internal counter (low byte)
        CLRF     TMR1H              ;Reset internal counter (high byte)
        BCF      PORTC, RST         ;Remove reset from external counter
        BSF      T1CON, TMR1ON      ;Open internal gate
        BSF      PORTC, GATE        ;Open external gate
```

Listing 11.3: Start of main loop

As always, the program starts by declaring numerous registers and bits (see **Listing 11.1**). Bits names starting with TMR and T1 are used to control the internal counter. The next stage is to initialise the registers and ensure that all gates are closed (**Listing 11.2**).

At this point, the program enters the main loop and the program reinitialises those registers that will need to be reinitialised every time a count is taken (**Listing 11.3**).

```
LOOP      MOVF     PORTC, W          ;Obtain Port C bit states
          IORLW    0xF0              ;Set digit to 15 (blank digit)
          MOVWF    PORTC             ;Clear Display
          INCF     DIGIT, W          ;Update digit number to be displayed
          ANDLW    0x07              ;Ensure within range 0 - 7
          MOVWF    DIGIT             ;Write back to digit number
          MOVWF    PORTA             ;Update 74LS138
          ADDLW    0x20              ;Data in registers 32-39 (0x20-0x27)
          MOVWF    FSR               ;Put address into indirect register
          SWAPF    INDR, W           ;Get BCD for next digit
          ANDLW    0xF0              ;Remove any extraneous bits
          MOVWF    CHAR              ;Store in temporary register
          MOVF     PORTC, W          ;Obtain Port C bit states
          ANDLW    0x0C              ;Remove BCD data
          IORWF    CHAR, W           ;Add new BCD data
          MOVWF    PORTC             ;Write back to port C


;Delay loop
          MOVLW    0xC8              ;Delay of 600us
          MOVWF    DELAY
LOOP1     DECFSZ   DELAY, F
          GOTO     LOOP1
          NOP                        ;Trimmer NOP


          MOVLW    0x7C              ;Delay of 372us
          MOVWF    DELAY
LOOP2     DECFSZ   DELAY, F
          GOTO     LOOP2
          NOP                        ;Trimmer NOP
          DECFSZ   LCOUNT, F         ;End of 100ms loop?
          GOTO     LOOP              ;No, do another 1ms loop
          MOVLW    0x1E              ;Yes, add final delay of 30us
          MOVWF    DELAY
SHORT     DECFSZ   DELAY, F
          GOTO     SHORT
          BCF      PORTC, GATE       ;Close external gate
          BCF      T1CON, TMR1ON     ;Close internal gate
```

Listing 11.4: Measure time and close gates   The count is now underway but the display has to be maintained until the gate is closed (**Listing 11.4**). Some explanations are necessary.

- The 74LS74 will blank the digit if it receives a code of 0x0F.
- Due to the nature of the low cost crystals that I use in my projects, it may be necessary to trim their frequency in both hardware and software. A fuller explanation of how to achieve this is given elsewhere in this project.
- In the program, most of this code (except for the last four instructions) is in a subroutine called TICK but it has been reformatted here to make explanation easier.

```
              MOVLW      3
              MOVWF      LCOUNT
   WAIT2      CALL       TICK
              DECFSZ     LCOUNT, F
              GOTO       WAIT2
```

Listing 11.5:
Maintaining the display after the gates are closed

After 100ms, the gates have been closed but the display routing is outputting digit 4 of the display. In order to avoid a visible blink on the display, it is necessary to display digits 5, 6 and 7 as shown in **Listing 11.5**. (See above for TICK subroutine).

After the seventh digit has been displayed, there is a 1ms period before digit 0 is due to be displayed. This time is used to translate the binary data into BCD. This is done using a subroutine called HEX2BCD, which decodes a byte (8 bits) of data, which must be in a register called HDATA. The most significant byte must be decoded first and then the other bytes in order. Currently, the most significant byte and the middle byte are being held in the internal counter registers (TMR1H and TMR1L) and the least significant byte is in the external (74HC4040) counter that is connected to port B. However, before it sends the data to be converted, the program clears the registers that will hold the BCD digits. **Listing 11.6** refers.

The binary to BCD conversion routine (**Listing 11.7**) is based on multiplying the data by two and adding the carry bit for each digit and for each bit of the binary number, working from least to most significant BCD digit and from most to least significant bit of the binary number. As soon as any digit becomes ten or more, ii is realigned by subtracting ten and adding one to the next higher digit. The binary number provides the carry bits for the first digit.

Listing 11.6:
Conversion calling routine

```
   CLRF      D0              ;Clear all digits
   CLRF      D1
   CLRF      D2
   CLRF      D3
   CLRF      D4
   CLRF      D5
   CLRF      D6
   CLRF      D7
   MOVF      TMR1H, W        ;Convert most significant byte
   MOVWF     HDATA
   CALL      HEX2BCD
   MOVF      TMR1L, W        ;Convert next significant byte
   MOVWF     HDATA
   CALL      HEX2BCD
   MOVF      PORTB, W        ;Convert least significant byte
   MOVWF     HDATA
   CALL      HEX2BCD
   CALL      BLANK           ;Blank leading zeros
   GOTO      LONG            ;Start 100ms loop all over again
```

```
HEX2BCD CLRF     HTEMP            ;Clear temporary data holding register
        CLRF     HOFFBIT          ;Set number of bits to zero

HLOOP   CLRF     HCARRY           ;Clear internal carry register
        CLRF     HOFFSET          ;Set digit number to zero
        BTFSC    HDATA, 7         ;Is bit 7 set?
        INCF     HCARRY, F        ;Yes so set internal carry register

HNXTDGT MOVF     HOFFSET, W       ;Obtain Next Digit from reg 32-39
        ADDLW    0x20             ;Add 32 to digit number
        MOVWF    FSR              ;Get data from that register

        BCF      STATUS, CARRY    ;Clear carry bit
        RLF      INDR, F          ;Multiply digit by two
        BTFSC    HCARRY, 0        ;Is internal carry register set?
        INCF     INDR, F          ;Yes, so add one to this digit
        MOVF     INDR, W          ;Start more than 10 check
        ADDLW    0x06             ;Add 6
        MOVWF    HTEMP            ;Store in temporary register
        CLRF     HCARRY           ;Prepare by clearing HCARRY
        BTFSS    HTEMP, 4         ;Is data > 10? (HTEMP > 16?)
        GOTO     HINCOFF          ;No, jump next three instructions
        INCF     HCARRY, F        ;Yes so set internal carry register
        MOVLW    0x0A             ;Subtract 10
        SUBWF    INDR, F

HINCOFF INCF     HOFFSET, F       ;Go to next decimal digit
        MOVLW    0x07             ;Start check for last digit
        SUBWF    HOFFSET, W
        BTFSS    STATUS, ZERO     ;Is it past last digit
        GOTO     HNXTDGT          ;No so do next decimal digit

HNXTBIT INCF     HOFFBIT, F       ;Yes so do next binary bit
        MOVLW    0x08             ;Start check for last bit
        SUBWF    HOFFBIT, W
        BTFSC    STATUS, ZERO     ;Is it past last bit
        RETURN                    ;Yes, all done so return
        RLF      HDATA, F         ;No so shift data
        GOTO     HLOOP            ;Go to next bit
```

Listing 11.7: Conversion routine This routine is a loop within a loop. The inner loop multiplies and checks each decimal digit whilst the outer loop applies each bit of the binary byte in turn. By calling the routine many times, with different data bytes and without clearing the digit registers between each call, multi-byte numbers can be converted.

```
BLANK    MOVF     D1, F              ;Check Digit 1 (Most significant)
         BTFSS    STATUS, ZERO       ;Is it zero
         RETURN                      ;No (no leading zeros) so return
         MOVLW    $0F                ;Yes (leading zero) so clear it
         MOVWF    D1
         MOVF     D2, F              ;Check Digit 2
         BTFSS    STATUS, ZERO       ;Is it zero
         RETURN                      ;No (no leading zeros) so return
         MOVLW    $0F                ;Yes (leading zero) so clear it MOVWF
D2
         MOVF     D3, F              ;Check Digit 3
         BTFSS    STATUS, ZERO       ;Is it zero
         RETURN                      ;No (no leading zeros) so return
         MOVLW    $0F                ;Yes (leading zero) so clear it
         MOVWF    D3
         MOVF     D4, F              ;Check Digit 4
         BTFSS    STATUS, ZERO       ;Is it zero
         RETURN                      ;No (no leading zeros) so return
         MOVLW    $0F                ;Yes (leading zero) so clear it
         MOVWF    D4
         RETURN
```

If a reading is not being taken, the display is likely to show a line of seven zeros. Therefore I decided to suppress leading zeros (**Listing 11.8**).

Listing 11.8: Leading zero blanking

Note that this will only clear the most significant four digits, leaving at least three digits even if the display is all zeros. This provides the most visually pleasing display. Clearing more digits just does not look right.

Aligning and setting the counter

Although the crystal frequency can be trimmed by changing the select on test capacitor or by using a trimmer capacitor, I found that some cheap crystals simply could not be pulled onto the correct frequency. It may be that I had encountered some faulty batches of crystals or it may be that the crystals were specified more for stability than for accuracy. Whatever it was, my choice was either using the cheap crystals or paying 15 times the price more for accurate ones. I chose the cheap option and made the changes in software.

There are two places where compensation can be made:

- In loop1 and loop2 by adding or removing NOP instructions or by changing the initial count values.
- In the routine called 'short'.

If you are using trimmer capacitors, set them to about half way. Then take a reading from a known frequency source, preferably above 10MHz. For every 3kHz that the value is off frequency, add or remove one from the value that is placed in a register called 'delay' immediately before either ' decfsz loop1' or 'decfsz loop2' (it doesn't matter which). Decrease the value to decrease the reading or increase the value to increase the reading. To change the value by approximately

1kHz, add or remove a NOP after the 'goto loop1' or 'goto loop2'. Again, add to increase the reading. You may have to change both loop values and NOPs to get it as accurate as you can. Then, for every 30Hz error, add or remove one from the value that is placed in a register called 'delay' immediately before 'decfsz short'. Finally, trim the capacitor for an accurate reading.

Options and enhancements

Other ranges

Although I have found that the 10Hz resolution to be adequate for most applications, the counter could be fitted with other ranges either as an alternative to the 10Hz range or in addition to it. For 1Hz or 100Hz resolution, simply change the count that is set in the instruction 'LONG   MOVLW'. At 1Hz resolution, it may also be necessary to extend the display to 8 digits although the current design would simply display the least significant seven digits without error.

For resolutions of 1kHz or higher, a slightly different approach is needed. This is to open the gate, wait the appropriate time and close the gate between each digit update of the display (**Listing 11.9**).

Once the count has been taken, consideration can be given to updating the display. This means converting the binary readings to decimal digits and outputting them to the display. It can be done for every reading without the display flickering too much or it can be left until a complete scan of the display has been completed.

For counters with multiple ranges I would strongly recommend having an independent program for each range with their own timing routines. Remember that the two programs must have different names for loops etc. This means that you cannot have a loop called 'loop1' in the short program if you have a 'loop1' in the long program. A common subroutine can be used for binary to BCD conversion. Then add a switch routine immediately after initialising the registers. For example **Listing 11.10**.

```
SHORT   BSF     PORTC, RST      ;Apply reset to external counter
        CLRF    TMR1L           ;Reset internal counter (low byte)
        CLRF    TMR1H           ;Reset internal counter (high byte)
        BCF     PORTC, RST      ;Remove reset from external counter
        BSF     T1CON, TMR1ON   ;Open internal gate
        BSF     PORTC, GATE     ;Open external gate
        CALL    MSDELAY         ;Call 1mS Delay (for kHz)
        BCF     PORTC, GATE     ;Close external gate
        BCF     T1CON, TMR1ON   ;Close internal gate
```

Listing 11.9: Short count times

```
SWITCH  BTFSS   PORTA, 3        ;Get status of switch
        GOTO    LONG            ;Go to 100ms range
        GOTO    SHORT           ;Go to 1ms range
```

Listing 11.10: Range switch routine

```
            MOVF     PORTB, W          ;Move port B to W
            SUBLW    0xE0              ;Subtract 0xE0 from lowest byte
            MOVWF    TEMP              ;Store in temporary register
            BTFSC    STATUS, CARRY     ;Check if carry
            GOTO     NEXT              ;No goto next byte
            DECF     TMR1L, F          ;Yes so decrement middle byte
            BTFSC    STATUS, CARRY     ;Check if this has gone negative
            GOTO     NEXT              ;No goto next byte
            DECF     TMR1H, F          ;Yes so decrement high byte


   NEXT     MOVLW    0x22              ;Subtract 0x22 from middle byte
            SUBWF    TMR1L, F
            BTFSS    STATUS, CARRY     ;Check if carry
            DECF     TMR1H, F          ;Yes
            MOVLW    0x02              ;No - subtract 0x02 from highest byte
            SUBWF    TMR1H, F
```

This assumes two ranges controlled by a single switch. Note that all 'GOTO LONG' and 'GOTO SHORT' references in the programs should be changed to 'GOTO SWITCH'. Adding this switch routine will not affect the accuracy of the count.

Listing 11.11: Offset frequency

Offset ranges

If the counter is being used with a VFO, such as in a transceiver project, it may be necessary to display a different frequency to the one that the counter is measuring. For example, a simple 80m transceiver with a 1.4MHz IF would have a VFO that tuned 4.9MHz to 5.2MHz (assuming a tuning range of 3.5MHz to 3.8MHz). In this example, the design should show the tuning range rather than the VFO range. To achieve this, take the reading as normal and then subtract 0x222E0 from the number. Remember to allow for the carry (or borrow) bit when undertaking this subtraction. **Listing 11.11** refers.

However, if the IF had been 9MHz, the VFO would have tuned 5.5MHz to 5.2MHz and in the wrong direction. This means that the highest VFO frequency corresponds to the lowest tuning frequency. Because there are no direct instructions to subtract a register from W or to subtract W from a literal, an indirect approach must be taken. This can be achieved either by writing the offset to registers and subtracting the reading from those registers, or by inverting the results of a SUBWF or SUBLW instructions. However, there is another way and I find this easier to use although it can be more difficult to understand:

- Complement the IF frequency. This can be done in PIC registers or manually and entered into the program.
- ADD this to the count
- Complement the result

By complementing, I mean change the ones to zero and the zeros to one. Eg:

- An IF of 9MHz with 10Hz steps is 900,000 steps.
- 900,000 is 0xDBBA0 (1101 1011 1011 1010 0000)
- The complement of 0xDBBA0 is 0x2445F (0010 0100 0100 0101 1111)

Full Listings

The complete program listing for this project can be found in the Appendix, and (together with other useful material) at www.rsgb.org/books /extra/picbasics.htm

129

```
          MOVF      PORTB, W          ;Move port B to temporary register
          ADDLW     0x5F              ;Add 0x5F to lowest byte
          MOVWF     TEMP              ;Store in temporary register
          BTFSS     STATUS, CARRY     ;Check if carry bit set from add
          GOTO      NEXT              ;No so go to next digit
          INCF      TMR1L, F          ;Yes, Increment middle byte
          BTFSS     STATUS, CARRY     ;Check if TMR1L overflowed
          GOTO      NEXT              ;No so go to next digit
          INCF      TMR1L, F          ;Yes, Increment high byte


NEXT      MOVLW     0x44              ;Load W with 0x44
          ADDWF     TMR1L, F          ;Add to middle byte
          BTFSC     STATUS, CARRY     ;Check if carry
          INCF      TMR1H, F          ;Yes so increment high byte
          MOVLW     0x02              ;Load W with 0x02
          ADDWF     TMR1H, F          ;Add to high byte


          COMF      TEMP, F           ;Invert low byte
          COMF      TMR1L, F          ;Invert middle byte
          COMF      TMR1H, F          ;Invert high byte
```

Listing 11.12: Reverse count

References

- *PICmicro Mid-Range MCU Family Reference Manual* (DS33023A) from www.microchip.com
- *16F87X Reference Manual* (DS30292C) from www.microchip.com
- *16F87XA Flash Memory Programming Specification* (DS35889B) from www.microchip.com
- *Application Note AN556* (Implementing a Table Read) from www.microchip.com
- *Application Note AN592* (Frequency Counter using PIC16C5X) from www.microchip.com
- 'UniCounter' (*QST* Dec 2000, page 33)

12

Project 6 - Digital voltmeter

T his voltmeter displays 11 to 16 volts to a precision of 10mV. It was designed to monitor the output of a 13.5 volt power supply. To this end, it has alarm signals if the voltage goes above 14.84 volts or below 12.28 volts.

Principles of operation

An 11 volt Zener diode drops the voltage being measured to a range of zero to five volts and this is fed into the 10 bit Analogue to Digital (A/D) converter of a 16F873 PIC. Using a +5.12V reference voltage, the PIC counts up to 1024 x 5mV steps using a reference voltage of 5.12 volts. In order to achieve this, the PIC must be run from a voltage that is slightly higher than the normal 5 volts because the reference voltage cannot be higher than the supply voltage.

This is done by placing a silicon diode in the common line of the voltage regulator and this adds 0.6 volts to the regulated output. Before being converted to decimal digits, the top two bits of the A/D conversion are used to generate an alarm signal. The under-voltage alarm is triggered if both bits are low and the over-voltage alarm if they are both high.

A figure equivalent to 11 volts is added to the binary count before converting it to decimal digits. These are sent one digit at a time and at approximately 1ms intervals, to a row of seven segment displays.

Multimeter front panel and . . .

. . . the board

Fig 12.1: Circuit diagram

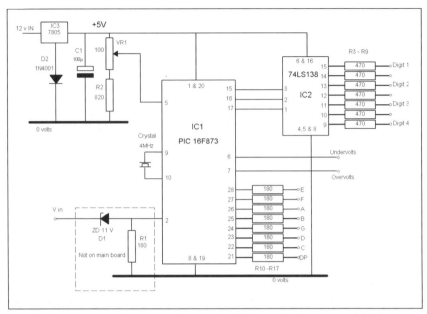

Component List	
IC1	PIC 16F873
IC2	74LS138
IC3	7805
D1	11.0 volt Zener diode
D2	1N4001
D3, D4	Red LEDs
Crystal	4MHz
R1	180Ω
R2	820Ω
R3 - R9	470Ω
R10 - R15	180Ω
VR1	100Ω preset
Misc.	2 x 14 pin or 1 x 28 pin by 0.3 inch IC holder
	1 x 16 pin IC holder
	Stripboard

Hardware

Details for the row of seven segment displays are given elsewhere in this book.

Fig 12.1 shows the voltmeter circuit diagram, **Figs 2.2 and 2.3** show the PCB and component positions and component values can be found in **Fig 12.4**.

Note that the Zener diode and 180Ω resistor are on a separate board.

Programming the PIC

Before use, the PIC will need to be programmed. The process for compiling PIC programs and for programming PIC chips is described elsewhere in this book.

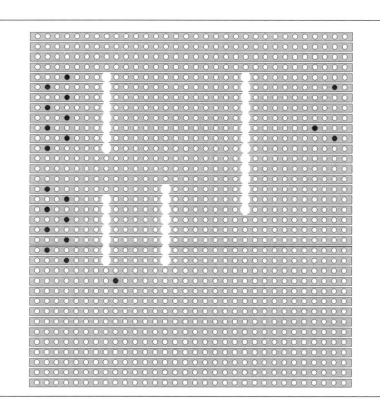

Fig 12.2: PCB cuts and pins

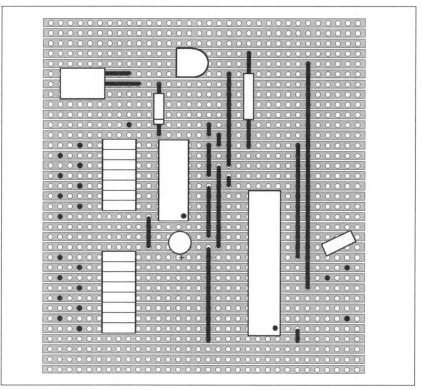

Fig 12.3: Wires and component positions

Fig 12.4: Component values

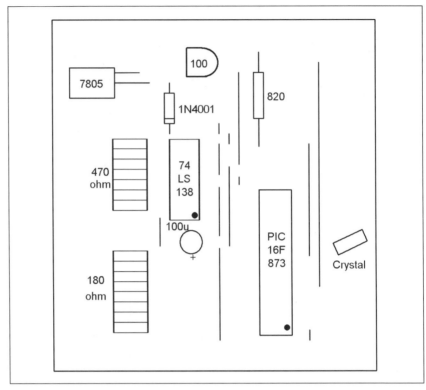

For this project, the configuration bits must be set for a high speed crystal oscillator. Both the watchdog timer and power-up timer must be disabled. Low voltage programming must also be disabled.

Software description

Listing 12.1: Declaring the registers

Much of the software for this project has been taken from previous projects. As always, the program starts by defining registers and bits (**Listing 12.1**) and initialising the registers (**Listing 12.2**).

```
    INDR    EQU     0x00    ;Indirect access to data in registers
    PCL     EQU     0x02    ;Program Counter
    STATUS  EQU     0x03    ;Used for Zero bit
    FSR     EQU     0x04    ;Address for indirect access
    PORTA   EQU     0x05    ;A/D input and LEDs
    PORTB   EQU     0x06    ;Character output
    PORTC   EQU     0x07    ;Digit number
    PCLATH  EQU     0x0A    ;Program Counter High Bits
    ADRES   EQU     0x1E    ;A/D Results (Data)
    ADCON   EQU     0x1F    ;A/D Converter control
    D7      EQU     0x20    ;Right hand digit
    D6      EQU     0x21
    D5      EQU     0x22
    D4      EQU     0x23
```

Listing continued opposite >

```
> Listing continued from previous page
D3        EQU        0x24
D2        EQU        0x25
D1        EQU        0x26
D0        EQU        0x27            ;Left hand digit
DIGIT     EQU        0x28            ;Digit number being displayed
COUNT     EQU        0x2B            ;Delay count
BINH      EQU        0x2D            ;Binary A/D high byte
BINL      EQU        0x2E            ;Binary A/D low byte
HDATA     EQU        0x30            ;Data for Binary to BCD
HTEMP     EQU        0x31            ;Temporary file used in Bin2BCD
HCARRY    EQU        0x32            ;Carry between BCD digits
HOFFSET   EQU        0x33            ;Digit number in Bin2BCD
HOFFBIT   EQU        0x34            ;Bit number in Bin2BCD
W         EQU        0
F         EQU        1
CARRY     EQU        0               ;Carry bit when dividing by 2
ZERO      EQU        2               ;Zero bit
GO        EQU        2               ;A/D start conversion
```

Listing 12.1: Declaring the registers

```
START     BSF        3, 5            ;Go to register bank 1
          MOVLW      0x0F            ;Set Port A bits 0-3 In, 4-7 Out
          MOVWF      PORTA
          CLRF       PORTB           ;Set Port B to all outputs
          MOVLW      0x0F            ;Set Port C bits 0-3 In, 4-7 Out
          MOVWF      PORTC
          MOVLW      0x85            ;Right justify reading, use External
          MOVWF      ADCON           ;Vref, A0+A1 for A/D use only
          BCF        3, 5            ;Go back to register bank 0
          MOVLW      0x40            ;Take A/D input from bit 0 of Port A
          MOVWF      ADCON
          CLRF       PCLATH          ;Clear high byte of program counter
          CLRF       DIGIT           ;Clear digit registers
          CLRF       D0
          CLRF       D1
          CLRF       D2
          CLRF       D3
          CLRF       D4
          CLRF       D5
          CLRF       D6
          CLRF       D7
          BSF        ADCON, 0        ;Switch A/D on
          CALL       DELAY           ;Allow initial delay
```

Listing 12.2: Inialising the registers

```
LOOP    BSF     ADCON, GO      ;Start A/D
        CALL    DELAY          ;Allow time to complete reading
        MOVF    ADRES, W       ;Get high byte
        MOVWF   BINH
```

Listing 12.3: Obtaining the first reading

```
        BSF     PORTA, 4       ;Switch off undervolts
        BSF     PORTA, 5       ;Switch off overvolts
        BTFSS   BINH, 0        ;Bit 0 set?
        GOTO    ISLOW          ;No (could be 00)
        BTFSC   BINH, 1        ;Bit 1 set?
        GOTO    NEXT           ;Yes, so OK
        BCF     PORTA, 4       ;Switch on undervolts
        GOTO    NEXT
ISLOW   BTFSS   BINH, 1        ;Bit 1 set?
        GOTO    NEXT           ;No, so OK
        BCF     PORTA, 5       ;Switch on overvolts
```

Listing 12.4: Under/over voltage detection

```
NEXT    BSF     3, 5           ;Go to register bank 1
        MOVF    ADRES, W       ;Read low A/D byte
        BCF     3, 5           ;Go to register bank 0
        MOVWF   BINL           ;Write data to BINL

        ADDLW   0x00           ;Used to clear carry bit
        RRF     BINH, F        ;Divide by two
        RRF     BINL, F        ;Divide by two
```

Listing 12.5: Obtaining a full reading

The first thing that the program does is to get a reading from the A/D converter (**Listing 12.3**).

Only the high byte is read at this time. This is so that a decision can be made on whether to light the under-voltage or over-voltage LEDs. **Listing 12.4** checks for the codes 00 and 11 in bits 0 and 1 of the BINH register.

Irrespective of whether the LEDs are switched on or off, the reading must be completed so that it can be displayed (**Listing 12.5**).

The reading is in multiples of 5mV but we need multiples of 10mV so the reading is divided by two, losing the least significant bit. However, in order to avoid introducing errors, the carry bit must be cleared. This cannot be cleared directly so a register containing 0x00 is rotated.

Eleven volts can now be added to the BIN registers (**Listing 12.6**). In order to get an accurate reading, it may be necessary to measure the actual voltage drop across the Zener diode. This should be multiplied by 100 because the measurement is in 10mV steps, and converted to hexadecimal. (11 volts is hex 0x044C).

```
        ADDLW      0x00                ;Used to clear carry bit
        MOVLW      0x4C                ;Add 0x4C to low byte
        ADDWF      BINL, F
        BTFSC      STATUS, CARRY       ;Check for overflow
        INCF       BINH, F             ;Inc high byte if overflow
        MOVLW      0x04                ;Add 0x04 to high byte
        ADDWF      BINH, F
```

Listing 12.6: Adding 11 volts

```
        CLRF       D0                  ;Clear BCD data registers
        CLRF       D1
        CLRF       D2
        CLRF       D3
        CLRF       D4
        CLRF       D5
        CLRF       D6
        CLRF       D7
        MOVF       BINH, W             ;Call Binary to BCD with high byte
        MOVWF      HDATA
        CALL       HEX2BCD
        MOVF       BINL, W             Call Binary to BCD with low byte
        MOVWF      HDATA
        CALL       HEX2BCD
```

Listing 12.7: The calling routine

After clearing the digit registers, the Binary to BCD routine is called by **Listing 12.7**.

The Binary to Binary Coded Decimal Digits subroutine is the same subroutine that was used in the 30MHz frequency counter. This is based on multiplying the data by two and adding the carry bit for each digit and for each bit of the binary number, working from least to most significant BCD digit and from most to least significant bit of the binary number. As soon as any digit becomes ten or more, ii is realigned by subtracting ten and adding one to the next higher digit.

The binary number provides the carry bits for the first digit. **Listing 12.8** refers.

This routine is a loop within a loop. The inner loop multiplies and checks each decimal digit whilst the outer loop applies each bit of the binary byte in turn. By calling the routine many times, with different data bytes and without clearing the digit registers between each call, multi-byte numbers can be converted.

The last task is to output the data to the seven segment display (**Listing 12.9**).

The translation table (**Listing 12.10**) is similar to the 'Clock for the Shack' project except that the letters U, T and C are not included in the code.

```
HEX2BCD CLRF      HTEMP           ;Clear temporary data holding register
        CLRF      HOFFBIT         ;Set number of bits to zero


HLOOP   CLRF      HCARRY          ;Clear internal carry register
        CLRF      HOFFSET         ;Set digit number to zero
        BTFSC     HDATA, 7        ;Is bit 7 set?
        INCF      HCARRY, F       ;Yes so set internal carry register


HNXTDGT MOVF      HOFFSET, W      ;Obtain Next Digit from reg 32-39
        ADDLW     0x20            ;Add 32 to digit number
        MOVWF     FSR             ;Get data from that register

        ADDLW     0x00            ;Used to clear carry bit
        RLF       INDR, F         ;Multiply digit by two
        BTFSC     HCARRY, 0       ;Is internal carry register set?
        INCF      INDR, F         ;Yes, so add one to this digit
        MOVF      INDR, W         ;Start more than 10 check
        ADDLW     0x06            ;Add 6
        MOVWF     HTEMP           ;Store in temporary register
        CLRF      HCARRY          ;Prepare by clearing HCARRY
        BTFSS     HTEMP, 4        ;Is data > 10? (HTEMP > 16?)
        GOTO      HINCOFF         ;No, jump next three instructions
        INCF      HCARRY, F       ;Yes so set internal carry register
        MOVLW     0x0A            ;Subtract 10
        SUBWF     INDR, F


HINCOFF INCF      HOFFSET, F      ;Go to next decimal digit
        MOVLW     0x07            ;Start check for last digit
        SUBWF     HOFFSET, W
        BTFSS     STATUS, ZERO    ;Is it past last digit
        GOTO      HNXTDGT         ;No so do next decimal digit


HNXTBIT INCF      HOFFBIT, F      ;Yes so do next binary bit
        MOVLW     0x08            ;Start check for last bit
        SUBWF     HOFFBIT, W
        BTFSC     STATUS, ZERO    ;Is it past last bit
        RETURN                    ;Yes, all done so return
        RLF       HDATA, F        ;No so shift data
        GOTO      HLOOP           ;Go to next bit
```

Listing 12.8: Binary to BCD

138

```
TICK    MOVLW   0xFF            ;Clear current display
        MOVWF   PORTB
        INCF    DIGIT, W        ;Update digit number
        ANDLW   0x03            ;Ensure not beyond end
        MOVWF   DIGIT           ;Store revised number
        SWAPF   DIGIT, W        ;Output to Port C bits 4-6
        MOVWF   PORTC
        MOVF    DIGIT, W        ;Get digit number
        ADDLW   0x20            ;Add Register Offset
        MOVWF   FSR             ;Use as indirect register address
        MOVF    INDR, W         ;Get BCD code
        ANDLW   0x0F            ;Remove any extraneous bits
        CALL    XTABLE          ;Convert to display data
        MOVWF   PORTB           ;Output to port B
        GOTO    LOOP            ;Do it all again
```

Listing 12.9: Data output routine

```
XTABLE  ADDWF   PCL, F
        RETLW   0x09            ;Zero
        RETLW   0xED            ;One
        RETLW   0x43            ;Two
        RETLW   0xC1            ;Three
        RETLW   0xA5            ;Four
        RETLW   0x91            ;Five
        RETLW   0x31            ;Six
        RETLW   0xCD            ;Seven
        RETLW   0x01            ;Eight
        RETLW   0x85            ;Nine
        RETLW   0xFE            ;10
        RETLW   0xFE            ;11
        RETLW   0xFE            ;12
        RETLW   0xFE            ;13
        RETLW   0xFE            ;14
        RETLW   0xFE            ;15
        RETLW   0xFE            ;16
```

Listing 12.10: Translation table

(Remember that the word TABLE or any word starting with TABLE is reserved in MPASM and must not be used in a program. It can, however, be used with TASM)

Options and enhancements

To adapt the meter for other applications it may be necessary to change the voltage reference and offset. For example, the meter can be used without an offset to measure zero to five volts in 10mV steps. By adding two equal resistors as a voltage divider and removing the divide by two instructions from the software, so the meter actually measures in 5mV steps, but will measure up to 10 volts in pseudo 10mV steps.

Reducing the reference voltage reduces the step size. For example, if the reference voltage is set at 1.024 Volts, the meter will measure up to 1 volt in 1mV steps.

No figures are given for the input impedance of the A/D converter or how this varies between chips. My own experiments suggest that it is somewhat over 1MΩ but I have not yet needed to rely on this.

The voltmeter can also form the basis for other projects that rely on measuring a voltage. For example, a VSWR meter measures the forward and reverse voltages from a unit that samples the current through a coaxial cable.

References

	Full Listings

The complete program listing for this project can be found in the Appendix, and (together with other useful material) at www.rsgb.org/books /extra/picbasics.htm

- *PICmicro Mid-Range MCU Family Reference Manual* (DS33023A) from www.microchip.com
- *16F87X Reference Manual* (DS30292C) from www.microchip.com
- *16F87XA Flash Memory Programming Specification* (DS35889B) from www.microchip.com
- *Application Note AN556* (Implementing a Table Read) from www.microchip.com
- *Application Note AN557* (4 Channel Voltmeter and Keyboard) from www.microchip.com
- For details on using a PIC as a VSWR meter, see 'PIC SWR Meter' (*QST* Dec 1999, page 40)

13

Project 7 - A PC-based audio recorder

Because my local *GB2RS* broadcast came at the same time as a scheduled contact, I used to record the bulletin and play it back afterwards. I would also record the Shipping Forecast before setting off for a visit to the coast. In fact, having a cassette recorder around was useful to record various things that I found on the air. So I missed my cassette tape recorder when it went faulty, and the growth of CDs and MP3s means that cassette tape recorders were becoming difficult to buy.

Then, a colleague from the radio club suggested that I use the PC sound card and its recording software. Unfortunately, I use that for another purpose and didn't want to keep changing plugs and volume settings.

So I hit on the idea of using a COM port on the PC, which I have brought up to a connector on my desk. This required me to convert the sound into a stream of characters and then to produce a PC based program to store the incoming data stream.

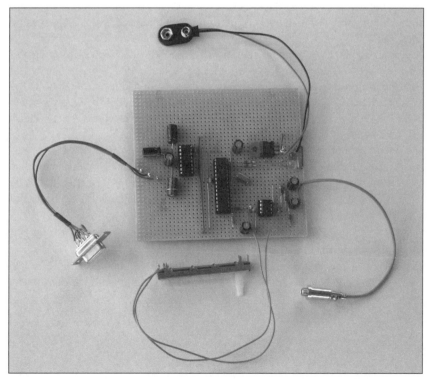

The hardware unit

This left two issues to be decided:

- How to digitise the signal.
- How to record the incoming data stream so that it could be replayed.

When digital telephones first became available, they produced 8000 x 8 bit samples per second, so I decided to use the same. That solved the first issue. Then I looked at the various audio file formats. The sound '.au' format (also known as '.snd' format) appeared to be the simplest and it is supported by my Microsoft Windows Media Player, so I decided to use that. Each file has a 24 byte header and can be any length up to 4,294,967,295 bytes - that's over six days worth of recording. What's more, a file can be edited for length by cutting it and adding exactly the same header to the new portion. There is no need to recalculate it or to cut the file at a specific place.

Having built this unit, I find now that I can use it for various other purposes such as digital signal processing (DSP).

Principles of operation

This project has two parts:

- An analogue to digital converter that plugs into the radio and a COM port on the computer.
- A program (RECPIC.EXE) that runs on the computer.

PIC board

The analogue to digital converter is based on a 16F73 chip. This has both an A/D converter and a UART. The UART generates a 10 bit serial signal that goes to the PC via a voltage converter. Audio could be picked up from the headphone socket but my transceivers have sockets on them that provide audio from before the volume control. These sockets are designed to be used with TNCs or radio modems.

The audio passes through an operational amplifier. This allows the volume to be controlled. Then it goes into an A/D port on the PIC. This is clocked at 20MHz simply because this frequency is directly divisible by 8000Hz and is close to the UART frequency. For the UART to transfer 8000 bytes per second, it must have a transmit speed of at least 80,000 bits per second. This is because a UART sends at least two extra bits for each byte:

- A start bit before each byte
- A stop bit after each byte. If the next character is not ready at the end of this period, the stop bit can be extended until it is. Therefore the stop bit can be any length as long as it is at least one bit in length. In addition, it does not need to be an exact number of bits.

Fig 13.1 shows a capital "S" (hex 0x53 or 01010011 binary). Note that the bits are sent with bit zero first.

Looking at my PC, the next easily available speed above 80,000 bps was 115,200 bits per second. At this speed, only a 20MHz crystal could provide a

Fig 13.1: Asynchronous waveform

signal that was within 2% of the desired speed for a reasonable cost. Other crystals were available but they were either expensive, at least 8% away from the

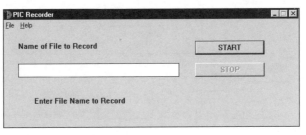

Fig 13.2: The PC program

UART frequency or not a multiple of 8000 samples per second.

The UART output from the PIC is at standard TTL levels of near zero volts for a logic zero and near five volts for a logic one. Unfortunately, the PC COM port uses a negative voltage for a logic one and a positive voltage for a logic 0. These voltages can be between 3 and 15 volts (and up to 25 volts in some circumstances) so a voltage converter is needed. For this project, I used a Maxim MAX202 chip.

PC program (RECPIC.EXE)

Upon starting the PC program (**Fig 13.2**), it prompts the user for a file name. It then creates the file and writes the header to it. This header comprises:

- A full stop and the letters s, n and d in lower case (.snd or 0x2e736e64 in hex).
- The value 0x00000016. This is a 32 bit number with a value of 24 decimal. It is the length of this header in bytes.
- The value 0xffffffff. This is the maximum length of the recording (6 days, 5 hours, 7 minutes, 50.9 seconds)
- The value 0x00000002. This is the recording format of 8 bits per sample with a linear A/D conversion
- The value 0x00001F40. (8000 decimal) This is the number of samples per second
- The value 0x00000001. This identifies the signal as being mono.

Note:
RECPIC.EXE can be downloaded from www.rsgb.org/books /extra/picbasics.htm

Then the program simply copies each character that it receives from the COM port to the file. However, it must first modify the value by subtracting 128 (0x80) from it. This is because the PIC works on values from zero volts to five volts. When there is no signal, 2.5 volts is present on the A/D pin of the PIC. An input signal adds to and subtracts from this 2.5 volt level.

The PC, on the other hand, expects a no signal value of zero. So if the signal has an amplitude of 400mV, the PIC will produce a value of 2.5 volts plus 400mV (=2.9 volts), which is 0x95 (0x80 plus 0x15). To produce the same effect on the PC, a value of 0x15 is needed. When the voltage goes negative with respect to the no-signal condition, the codes go negative. So if the signal has an amplitude of 400mV and it is at its most negative going phase then the PIC will produce a value of 2.5 volts minus 400mV (=2.1 volts), which is 0x6B (0x80 minus 0x15). To produce the same effect on the PC, a value of 0xEB is needed, which is zero minus 0x15.

Interface

A simple three wire interface is used between the A/D converter unit and the PC. This is because no flow control is used.

Fig 13.3: Circuit diagram

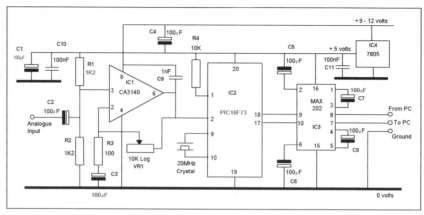

Hardware

The unit is mounted on a piece of stripboard. It was not found necessary to tune the crystal onto its exact frequency.

R1 and R2 must be equal in value so they bias the operational amplifier to about 2.5 volts. For connecting to an in-circuit point on the transceiver, each resistor should be approximately twice the output impedance so that the two resistors in parallel are equal to that impedance.

Where the unit will be connected in parallel with headphones, the impedance becomes unimportant as long as it is above about 250 ohms. The components shown above provide an impedance match into 600 ohms and I have not found any cases where this is unacceptable.

Component List	
IC1	CA3140 or any 741 equivalent
IC2	PIC 16F73 (or 16F873)
IC3	MAX202 (or MAX212)
IC4	L7805CV
C1-C8	100µF 16V or any value above 22µF
C9	1nF
C10, C11	100nF
R1, R2	1.2kΩ
R3	100Ω
R4	10kΩ
VR1	10KΩ logarithmic
Crystal	20MHz
Misc.	2 x 14 pin IC holders
	16 pin IC holder
	8 pin IC holder
	9 way 'D' type socket
	Audio connector to suit radio.
	Wire
	Pins (Optional)

Component layouts

The board cuts, wire and component layout and component values are in **Figs 13.4 to 13.6**.

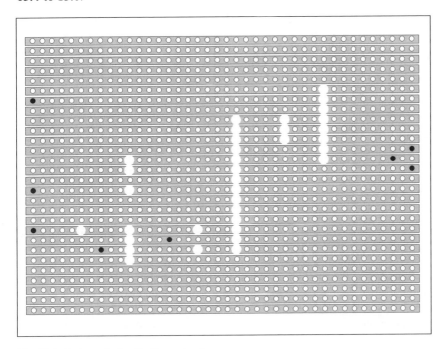

Fig 13.4: Cuts and pins (bottom view).

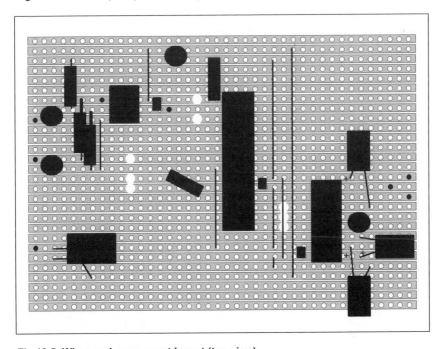

Fig 13.5: Wires and component layout (top view)

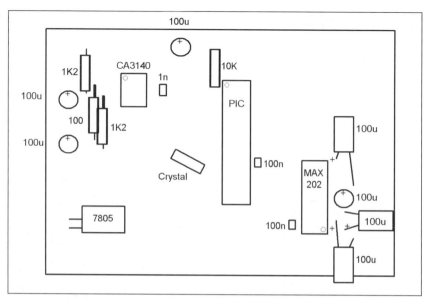

Fig 13.6: Component values

Programming the PIC

Before use, the PIC will need to be programmed. The process for compiling PIC programs and for programming PIC chips is described elsewhere in this book.

For this project, the configuration bits must be set for a high speed crystal oscillator and both the watchdog timer and power-up timer must be disabled.

Software operation

Note that anything that comes on a line that is after a semi-colon is a comment and does not affect the program in any way.

Listing 13.1: Register declaration

The first stage is to declare some register and bit names **Listing 13.1**. This makes it easier to read the program.

```
        STATUS    EQU      0x03              ;Used for Zero bit
        PORTA     EQU      0x05
        PORTC     EQU      0x07
        TXSTA     EQU      0x18
        SPBRG     EQU      0x19
        RCSTA     EQU      0x18
        TXREG     EQU      0x19
        ADRES     EQU      0x1E
        ADCON     EQU      0x1F
        TIMER1    EQU      0x21
        COUNT     EQU      0x22
        TEMP      EQU      0x23
        W         EQU      0
        F         EQU      1
        GO        EQU      2
        ZERO      EQU      2
```

```
BSF         3, 5
BCF         3, 6
MOVLW       0xC0
MOVWF       PORTC           ;PORTC = Output except UART
MOVLW       0xFF
MOVWF       PORTA           ;PORTA = Input
```

Listing 13.2: Port initialisation

```
MOVLW       0x0A
MOVWF       SPBRG           ;Set Baud Rate to 115200
BSF         TXSTA, 2        ;Set Baud Rate to High
BCF         TXSTA, 4        ;Set Asynchronous operation
BCF         3, 5
BSF         RCSTA, 7        ;Enable the UART serial port
BSF         3, 5
BSF         TXSTA, 5        ;Enable the transmitter
```

Listing 13.3: UART initialisation

Then, the ports are initialised (**Listing 13.2**). Only port A and port C are used. Port C is initialised as all outputs except for the UART bits (bits 6 and 7) which must be initialised as inputs. Port A, which contains the analogue inputs, is initialised as inputs.

After initialising the ports, the UART is initialised next (see **Listing 13.3**). Note that only the transmitter is enabled. This project does not use the receiver but, if it did, it would have to be enabled with a 'BSF RCSTA, 4' instruction. This command must come immediately after the "BSF, RCSTA, 7" instruction and before changing register banks with the 'BSF 3,5' instruction. After enabling the UART, the Analogue to Digital (A/D) converter is initialised (**Listing 13.4**).

The minimum number of bits that can be set to Analogue use is two (bits 0 & 1 of port A). A value of 0x04, when written to the ADCON register in register bank 1, sets this and also sets the reference voltage to be the 5 volt supply. The program then changes register bank and writes a value of 0x80 to the ADCON register in register bank 0. A value of 0x080 sets the clocking rate to $1.6\mu S$, which is the fastest clocking rate that the PIC allows. This sets the conversion time to $14.4\mu s$ ($9 \times 1.6\mu s$). The value of 0x80 also sets the converter so that it converts the input on bit 0 of port A. In accord with PIC recommendations, the A/D converter is not switched on at the same time as it is configured but immediately after it, with a 'BSF ADCON, 0' instruction.

```
MOVLW       0x04            ;Set bits 0 & 1 of port A as Analogue
MOVWF       ADCON
BCF         3, 5
MOVLW       0x80            ;Set A/D clock to osc/32 & use bit 0
MOVWF       ADCON
BSF         ADCON, 0        ;Switch on A/D converter
```

Listing 13.4: A/D initialisation

```
LOOP    MOVLW     0x10          ;Delay 16 x 3 = 48 instructions
        MOVWF     TIMER1
T0      DECFSZ    TIMER1, F
        GOTO      T0


        BSF       ADCON, GO     ;Start A/D conversion process
        NOP                     ;Trimmer NOPs
        NOP


        MOVLW     0xBE          ;Delay 190 x 3 = 570 instructions
        MOVWF     TIMER1
T1      DECFSZ    TIMER1, F
        GOTO      T1


        MOVF      ADRES, W      ;Read result of A/D conversion
        MOVWF     TXREG         ;Write to UART transmitter
        GOTO      LOOP
```

Listing 13.5: Main loop

After being switched on, the A/D converter requires time to take a reading and then further time to decode it. An initial delay of 9.6μs (48 instructions) is made to allow a voltage settling time before the 'GO' bit is set on the A/D converter. Then a 114μs delay is made, which is more than enough time to take the reading. However, the overall loop time, of 125μs (625 instructions) is based on the design speed, which is a compromise between file size and quality of encoded speech. At the end of this delay period, the reading is taken and immediately written to the UART transmitter. (**Listing 13.5** refers). The program then loops back to take another reading.

Enhancements

Although the gain control (VR1) could be set by trial and error, I found it helpful to add two LEDs (one green and one red) as visible indicators of the volume (**Fig 13.7**). Each LED is wired in series with a 470Ω resistor from the positive line to port C on the PIC. The red LED is connected to bit 3 (pin 14) and the green LED to bit 2 (pin 13).

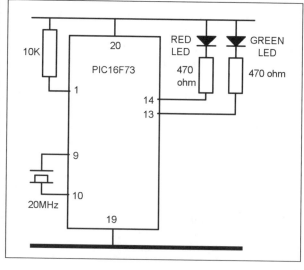

Fig 13.7: LED volume indicators

```
          MOVLW     0xBB              ;Value reduced from 0xBE
          MOVWF     TIMER1            ;No change from previous listing
   T1     DECFSZ    TIMER1, F         ;No change from previous listing
          GOTO      T1                ;No change from previous listing

          MOVLW     $0C               ;Switch off LEDs
          MOVWF     PORTC

          MOVF      ADRES, W          ;No change from previous listing
          MOVWF     TXREG             ;No change from previous listing

          ANDLW     0xF0              ;Zero least significant 4 bits
          ADDLW     0x10              ;If W = 0xF0 it now contains 0x00
          BTFSC     STATUS, ZERO      ;Check if zero
          BCF       PORTC, RED        ;Yes so switch on RED LED
          ADDLW     $10               ;If W originally held 0xE0. Now = 0x00
          BTFSC     STATUS, ZERO      ;Check if zero
          BCF       PORTC, GREEN      ;Yes so switch GREEN LED on

          GOTO      LOOP              ;From previous listing
```

Listing 13.6: Volume detection

The green light is triggered when the volume reaches 224 decimal (0xE0 hex or 87.5% of full volume) and the red light is triggered at a volume of 240 decimal (0xF0 hex or 93.75% of full volume). This is achieved by adding an additional routine between the write to UART instruction and the looping instruction at the end of the program. But first, the LEDs must be switched off. This is done by writing 0x0C to port C. **Listing 13.6** refers.

The value read from the A/D converter and written to the UART is still in the W register so it can be tested. For example, if the value is 0xF3 it is first 'AND'ed with 0xF0 to remove the least significant four bits. This means that the value in W is now 0xF0.

Then 0x10 is added so the value is now 0x00. A check on the zero bit (or the carry bit) then reveals that the original value was more than 0xF0. However, if the original value was say 0xE7, then it is 'AND'ed to produce 0xE0 and 0x10 is added. This results in a value of 0xF0, which will not trigger the zero or carry bits of the status register. Therefore, the instruction to turn on the red LED is skipped but another 0x10 is added. This time, the result is zero so the green LED is switched on.

These additional 9 instructions mean that the time delay loop must be recalculated so the value loaded into Timer 1 as part of the T1 loop is reduced to 0xBB.

References

- *PICmicro Mid-Range MCU Family Reference Manual* (DS33023A) from www.microchip.com
- *16F87X Reference Manual* (DS30292C) from www.microchip.com

Full Listings

The complete program listing for this project can be found in the Appendix, and (together with other useful material) at www.rsgb.org/books /extra/picbasics.htm

- *16F87XA Flash Memory Programming Specification* (DS35889B) from www.microchip.com
- *Application Note AN556* (Implementing a Table Read) from www.microchip.com
- 'DDS for Radio Projects' (*RadCom* Nov 2000, page 16)
- 'Serial Port A/D converter for DSP' (*RadCom* April 1997, page 37)

14

Project 8 - Morse decoder

T his unit was designed to allow those who cannot read Morse-code, to help with logging during CW contests. Like all Morse decoders, it works best with code that has been sent by a machine or a good CW operator. It doesn't like code where the timing varies. After some experimentation, it was found that having a timing control seemed to allow the operator to latch on to the signal more quickly than an automatic decoder would. As an additional aid to learning and to help setting the instrument, the incoming signal can be displayed as dots and dashes or as alphanumeric text on a 16 character display.

Principles of Operation

An LM567 phase locked loop (PLL) chip converts the audio signal into a logic signal that is low when the Morse signal is present and high when it is not. This circuit was taken from the LM datasheet. The signal is fed into the PIC, which samples the signal every three milliseconds or so.

The PIC is looking for places where the signal changes or where the signal has been absent for a long time, as this could be the end of an over. When a signal disappears, the PIC must decide whether it was a dot, a dash, or a spurious signal. Spurious signals are caused by the PLL locking onto noise, and these

pulses are very short (usually less than 8 sample times). Dots are differentiated from dashes by comparing the time to a variable figure that is derived by reading a potentiometer, using the PIC's analogue to digital (A/D) function. Dots are shorter than this time whereas dashes are longer.

The PIC also needs to measure the spaces between the dot/dash elements. As happens with spurious signals, very short periods are ignored. Short periods are the spaces between the dots and dashes that make up a single character. A longer period indicates the end of a character and this is the signal for the PIC to decode and display it. However, there is also an even longer time and this is the space between words. In this case, after the character is decoded, an extra space character is inserted.

Character decode is achieved through table reads. The first read is based on the number of dots or dashes. There is a subsequent table for each length from one dot or dash through to six dot/dash combinations.

This character is then sent to the alpha-numeric display, which operates in 8 bit interface mode. Only one line of text is used due to the difficulties with addressing two lines in scrolling mode. Characters are entered at the right of the line and all other characters move one place to the left. This was found to be the most pleasing form of display.

As an alternative, the dots and dashes can be sent to the display. The unit is switched between character mode and dot/dash mode by a switch that is connected to bit 4 of Port A.

Using the Morse Decoder

When the Morse Decoder is switched on, it will display the message 'CW Decoder'. Adjust the preset potentiometer on the PIC board so that this message can easily be read.

The decoder is designed to be connected to the TNC port of a transceiver. It could also be connected in parallel with headphones or the speaker although some care may be needed to make a safe connection. It is designed to operate with a signal of 100mV upwards. Although it could be fed from an amplified microphone, this was found to be unsatisfactory in practice due to the high level of background noise.

Once a CW signal is heard on the receiver, tune the frequency control of the Morse Decoder until the LED flashes in sympathy with the incoming signal. Then turn the speed control until the Morse is being decoded. If lots of 'E's and 'T's are being displayed, the speed control has been set too fast. Alternatively the unit can be switched to dot/dash mode and the speed adjusted for correct decoding. However, in practice, this is only useful for slow Morse. At faster speeds, the dots and dashes appear to fast for the brain to coordinate them with the sounds that are being heard. This is because there is a slight delay between the end of a dot or dash and the display being updated.

Hardware

The unit was built on two pieces of stripboard. One holds the PIC and the other contains the phase locked loop. Note that the strips run in different directions on the two boards.

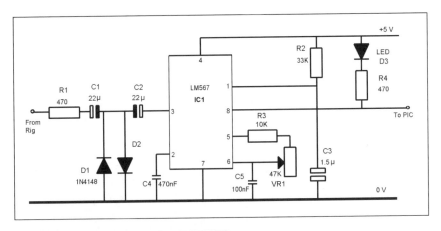

Fig 14.1: PLL board circuit diagram

Component List for the PLL board	
IC1	LM567
D1, D2	1N4148
D3	Red LED
R1	470Ω
R2	33kΩ
R3	10kΩ
R4	470Ω
VR1	47kΩ
C1, C2	22µF, 16V
C3	1.5µF, non-polarized
C4	470nF
C5	100nF

Fig 14.2: PLL board cuts and pins

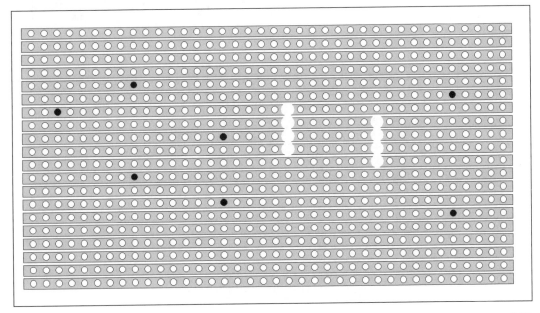

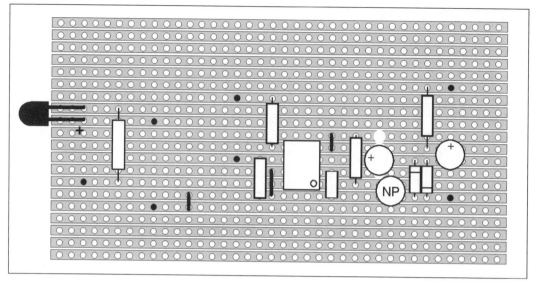

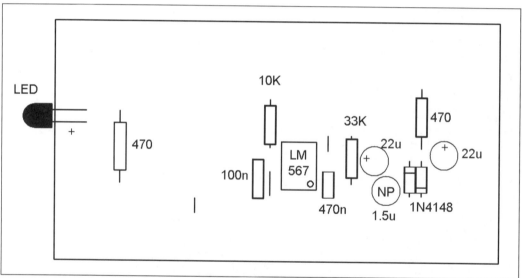

Component List for the PIC Board	
IC1	PIC16F873 (or 16F73)
IC2	TS7805
Crystal	4MHz
R1, R2	10kΩ
VR1	10kΩ preset
VR2	22kΩ linear potentiometer
C1	100µF
C2	22µF
Switch	Single pole slide switch.

(Top) Fig 14.3: PLL board layout

(Middle) Fig 14.4: PLL board component values

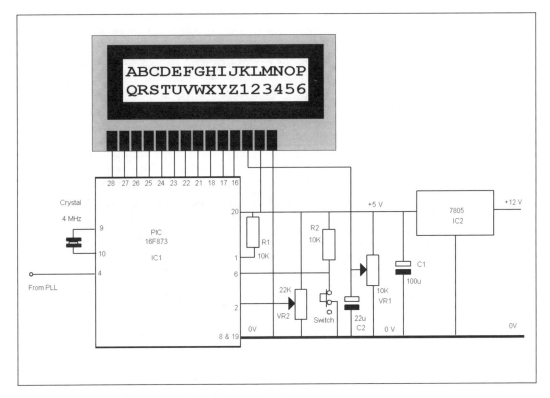

Fig 14.5: PIC board circuit diagram

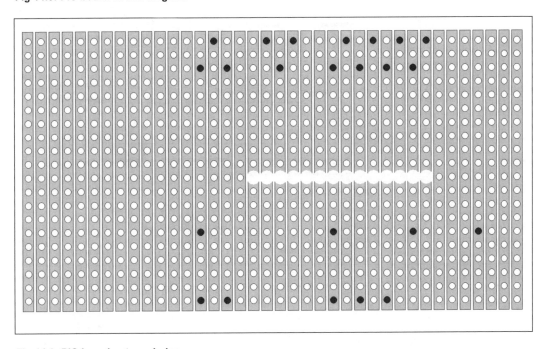

Fig 14.6: PIC board cuts and pins

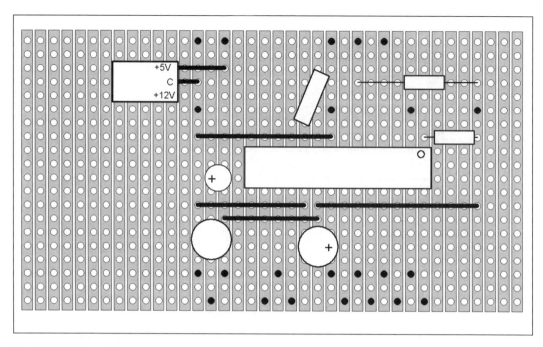

Fig 14.7: PIC board layout

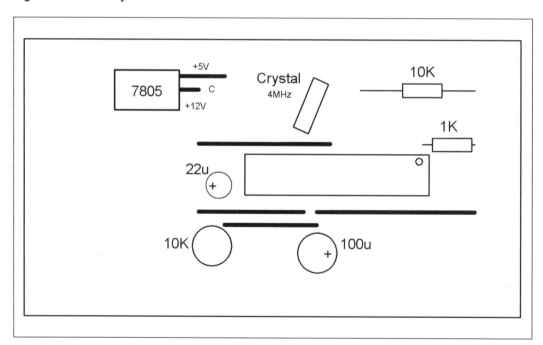

Fig 14.8:PIC board component values

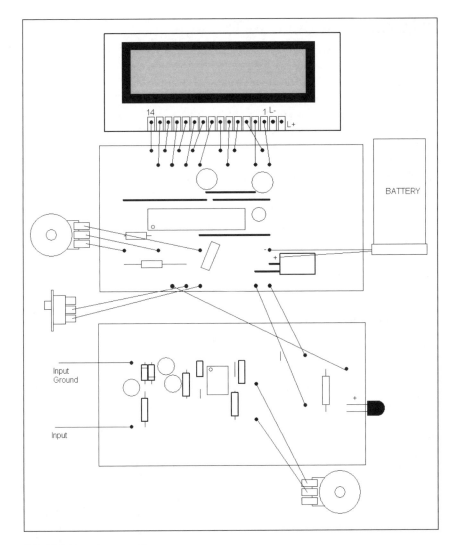

Fig 14.9: Board connections

Display

A two line by 16 character display was used in the original.

Construction

The boards are connected together so that they can be concertinaed into a box. **Fig 14.9** shows how the boards are interconnected. Note the way that pins 2 and 3 of the display are connected to the PIC board.

Programming the PIC

Before use, the PIC will need to be programmed. The process for compiling PIC programs and for programming PIC chips is described elsewhere in this book.

For this project, the configuration bits must be set for a crystal oscillator. Both the watchdog timer and power-up timer must be disabled.

Adjusting the Decode Timings

The unit will work with Morse speeds from about 5 words per minute up to about 25 words per minute, as long as the timings are fairly accurate. This is based on a 3ms loop and a count from 12 to 70 cycles through the loop. Anything less than the count is decoded as a dot or inter-bit space whilst longer pulses are decoded as a dash or inter-character gap. To change the timing, modify the number of times that the delay routine is called from the SP1 and MK1 routines.

The unit is not good at decoding 'slow' Morse where the code is sent at one speed but the gaps between characters are extended. For this, the number of times that the delay routine is called from the SP1 routine must be extended. This will normally handle machine sent 'slow' Morse, where all of the gaps are extended. In cases where the inter-bit gaps are kept short but the inter-character gaps are extended, the decoder will normally decode this without any changes but it will see the long gaps as being inter-word gaps. Although the timing could be adjusted I have found that the spaces do not affect the readability at these low speeds.

Software Operation

Note that if a line is preceded by a semi-colon, anything on the line is a comment and does not affect the program in any way.

As always, the program starts by declaring register and bit names (**Listing 14.1**). These simply make the program easier to read. Thn the program initialises the ports, the A/D converter and the display (**Listings 14.2 to 14.4**).

The 'display initial text' sequence has been shortened for clarity. Note the delays that are used in initialising the displays. These are essential and the display will not work if data or commands are sent too close to each other. The delay subroutine actually waits for about 1ms each time that it is called and it includes a read of the potentiometer that is connected to the A/D converter. The value read is stored in the register called 'speed' (**Listing 14.5** refers).

Although the potentiometer reading can go from zero to 255, the reading is divided by four by shifting it right twice. Twelve is then added to the result. This means that the count, that determines whether the reading is a dot or a dash can vary from 12 to 70. It must also be noted that the delay routine is called three times for every increment in the count.

When writing to the display, two other subroutines are used:

- WC writes commands to the display
- WD writes data to the display

These routines are the same except for the command that sets the Data/Command line (**Listings 14.6 and 14.7**).

Having initialised the PIC and the display, the program checks the input (**Listing 14.8**). It assumes that no signal is present.

Note that the input signal is active low. This means that the input is low when the Morse signal is present and the LED of the PLL board is lit. The input is high when the signal is absent and the LED is out. Therefore, the BTFSS instruction will skip if the signal is absent. If the signal is present, there has been a change in state, so the MARK routine (**Listing 14.9**) can be called.

```
;PIC Registers
PCL         EQU     0x02            ;Program Counter low byte
STATUS      EQU     0x03            ;Used for Zero and Carry bits
PORTA       EQU     0x05            ;Inputs from PLL, A/D and Switch
PORTB       EQU     0x06            ;Data output to display
PORTC       EQU     0x07            ;Control signals to display
PCLATH      EQU     0x0A            ;Program Counter high byte
ADRES       EQU     0x1E            ;A/D data register
ADCON       EQU     0x1F            ;A/D control, register


;User Defined Registers
MARKREG     EQU     0x20            ;Dot/Dash signal
SPACEREG    EQU     0x21            ;Space between dots/dashes
MORSE       EQU     0x24            ;Character
MORSELEN    EQU     0x25            ;Quantity of dots/dashes
SPEED       EQU     0x28            ;From potentiometer setting
T1          EQU     0x2C            ;Part of delay loop
T2          EQU     0x2D            ;Part of delay loop


;PIC Bits
W           EQU     0
F           EQU     1
ZERO        EQU     2
CARRY       EQU     0
ADON        EQU     0               ;Switches A/D converter on
GO          EQU     2               ;Starts A/D conversion


;User Defined Bits
ENABLE      EQU     7               ;Strobe to display
RW          EQU     6               ;Read/Write to display
DC          EQU     5               ;Data/Command to display
INPUT       EQU     2               ;Input from PLL
SWITCH      EQU     4               ;Character/dot-dash switch
```

Listing 14.1: Register initialisation

```
START   BSF     3, 5        ;Switch to register bank 1
        MOVLW   0xFF
        MOVWF   PORTA       ;Set Port A to all inputs
        CLRF    PORTB       ;Set Port B to all outputs
        CLRF    PORTC       ;Set Port C to all outputs
```

Listing 14.2: Port initialisation

159

```
        ;Initialise A/D convertor


                MOVLW       0x04        ;Analogue on bits 0 & 1 of port A
        plus
                MOVWF       ADCON       ;internal voltage reference
                BCF         3, 5        ;Switch to register bank 0
                MOVLW       0x40        ;Set A/D input on bit 0 plus
                MOVWF       ADCON       ;Left justify (8 bit) conversion
                BSF         ADCON, 0    ;Start A/D converter
```

Listing 14.3: A/D converter initialisation

```
        ;Initialise Display
                MOVLW       0x28        ;Initial delay (40mS)
                MOVWF       T2
        I2      CALL        DELAY
                DECFSZ      T2, F
                GOTO        I2
                MOVLW       0x30        ;Function Set (8 bit I/F, 1 line)
                CALL        WC
                CALL        DELAY
                MOVLW       0x0F        ;Display On
                CALL        WC
                CALL        DELAY
                MOVLW       0x01        ;Clear Display
                CALL        WC
                CALL        DELAY
                CALL        DELAY
                CALL        DELAY
                MOVLW       0x07        ;Entry Mode (Scrolling from right)
                CALL        WC
                CALL        DELAY
                MOVLW       0x8F        ;Set Cursor Position (to right edge)
                CALL        WC
                CALL        DELAY
        ;Display initial text
                MOVLW       0x43        ;Letter C
                CALL        WD
                CALL        DELAY
                MOVLW       0x57        ;Letter W
                CALL        WD
                CALL        DELAY
```

Listing 14.4:Initialise display and display initial text

160

```
;Delay routine (includes read of potentiometer)
DELAY   MOVLW    0xA6             ;166 (x3) = 498uS (A/D settling time)
        MOVWF    T1
D1      DECFSZ   T1, F
        GOTO     D1
        BSF      ADCON, GO        ;Start A/D conversion
        MOVLW    0xA5             ;165 (x 3) = 485uS (A/D convert time)
        MOVWF    T1
D2      DECFSZ   T1, F
        GOTO     D2
        RRF      ADRES, W         ;Read and shift A/D result
        MOVWF    SPEED            ;Write to speed register
        RRF      SPEED, F         ;Shift another bit
        MOVLW    0x3F             ;Reduce to 6 bits
        ANDWF    SPEED
        MOVLW    0x0C             ;Add 12 (Speed = 12 to 76)
        ADDWF    SPEED               ;Store in speed register
        RETURN
```

Listing 14.5: Delay and A/D read

Listing 14.6: Write Command routine

```
;Write command routine
WC      MOVWF    PORTB
        MOVLW    0x00
        MOVWF    PORTC
        BSF      PORTC, ENABLE
        NOP
        BCF      PORTC, ENABLE
        BSF      PORTC, RW
        RETURN
```

```
;Write data routine
WD      MOVWF    PORTB            ;Data/Command to port B
        MOVLW    0x20             ;Set Data/Command line
        MOVWF    PORTC
        BSF      PORTC, ENABLE    ;Set Enable/Strobe bit
        NOP
        BCF      PORTC, ENABLE    ;Remove Enable/Strobe bit
        BSF      PORTC, RW        ;Set read mode
        RETURN
```

Listing 14.7: Write Data routine

161

```
SP1      BTFSS      PORTA, INPUT     ;Check input line. It signal present?
         GOTO       MARK             ;Yes, so go to mark routine
         INCF       SPACEREG, F      ;No so count length of space
         BTFSC      SPACEREG, 7      ;Is space very long?
         GOTO       LONG             ;Yes, so go to long routine
         CALL       DELAY            ;No, so wait 3mS longer
         CALL       DELAY
         CALL       DELAY
         GOTO       SP1              ;Loop
```

Listing 14.8: Space routine

```
MARK     CLRF       MARKREG          ;Clear the space count register
         MOVLW      0x06             ;Check length of space count register
         SUBWF      SPACEREG, W      ;First, check if very short
         ANDLW      0x80
         BTFSS      STATUS, ZERO
         GOTO       MK1              ;Too short = glitch
         GOTO       ACTION

;Action Routine - end of a space
ACTION   MOVF       SPEED, W         ;Get potentiometer value
         SUBWF      SPACEREG, F      ;Subtract from space count
         MOVF       SPACEREG, W
         ANDLW      0x80             ;Get positive/negative bit
         BTFSS      STATUS, ZERO     ;Test
         GOTO       MK1              ;Short = inter-bit gap (ignore)
         CALL       DECODE           ;Long so decode character
         MOVF       SPEED, W         ;Get potentiometer value (again)
         CLRF       MORSE            ;Clear morse character
         CLRF       MORSELEN
         SUBWF      SPACEREG, W      ;Subtract from space count (again)
         ANDLW      0x80             ;Get positive/negative bit
         BTFSS      STATUS, ZERO     ;Test
         GOTO       MK1              ;Short = inter-char gap (no more to do)
         MOVLW      0x20             ;Long = Inter word gap
         CALL       WD               ;Write space character to display
         GOTO       MK1
```

Listing 14.9: Mark routine

162

```
SPCE      CLRF      SPACEREG        ;Clear the space count register
          MOVLW     0x06            ;Check length of mark count register
          SUBWF     MARKREG, W      ;First, check if very short
          ANDLW     0x80
          BTFSS     STATUS, ZERO
          GOTO      SP1             ;Too short = glitch
          GOTO      DOTDASH


DOTDASH   INCF      MORSELEN, F     ;Increment character length
          MOVF      SPEED, W        ;Get potentiometer value
          SUBWF     MARKREG, W      ;Subtract from mark count
          ANDLW     0x80            ;Get positive/negative bit
          BTFSS     STATUS, ZERO    ;Positive = Dot. Negative = Dash
          GOTO      DOT             ;Dot
          GOTO      DASH            ;Dash
```

Listing 14.10: Space and Dot/Dash routines

```
DASH      RLF       MORSE, F        ;Move morse character one bit left
          BSF       MORSE, 0        ;Set bottom bit
          GOTO      SP1             ;Continue waiting for an edge
```

Listing 14.11: Simplified Dash routine

```
DASH      RLF       MORSE, F        ;Move morse character one bit left
          BSF       MORSE, 0        ;Set bottom bit
          BTFSS     PORTA, SWITCH   ;Get switch state
          GOTO      SP1             ;Character mode - so go to SP1
          MOVLW     0x2D            ;Dot/dash mode so create dash
          CALL      WD              ;Send to Display
          CLRF      MORSE           ;Delete morse character
          CLRF      MORSELEN
          GOTO      SP1             ;Continue waiting for an edge
```

Listing 14.12: Dash routine with dot/dash display

The aim of the SP1 routine is to time the length of the space. There is also an MK1 routine, which similar in that it times the mark signals. Both routines limit their count to 128 but, with the space routine, there could still be a character awaiting decoding so the 'long' routine checks this. It does this by checking the value of the 'morselen' register. If this is zero there is no character waiting, but any other value will cause the data to be decoded and displayed.

Like the SPACE routine, the MARK routine starts by clearing a register. Although this isn't needed for the MARK routine, it needs to be cleared now so the length of the mark pulse can be timed. The MARK routine then looks at the

```
.3DECODE        CALL        XTABLE      ;Call translate tables
        MOVWF   MORSE               ;Is it a character
        MOVF    MORSE, F
        BTFSC   STATUS, ZERO        ;Check if zero
        GOTO    OUT1                ;Bad character do go to out1
        MOVF    MORSE, W            ;Good character
        CALL    WD                  ;Write data to display
OUT1    CLRF    MORSE               ;Clear character
        CLRF    MORSELEN            ;Zeroise length
        RETURN

;Translation tables
        ORG     0x100               ;Place program at address 0x100
XTABLE  MOVLW   0x01                ;Set high program counter
        MOVWF   PCLATH
        MOVF    MORSELEN, W         ;Get character length
        ANDLW   0x07                ;Max 7 dot/dash combinations
        ADDWF   PCL, F              ;Add to program counter
        RETLW   0x00                ;No dot/dash
        GOTO    XTABLE1             ;One dot or dash
        GOTO    XTABLE2             ;Two dot/dashes
        GOTO    XTABLE3             ;Three dot/dashes
        GOTO    XTABLE4             ;Four dot/dashes
        GOTO    XTABLE5             ;Five dot/dashes
        GOTO    XTABLE6             ;Six dot/dashes
        RETLW   0x00                ;Seven dot/dashes = error

XTABLE3 MOVF    MORSE, W
        ANDLW   0x07
        ADDWF   PCL, F
        RETLW   0x53                ;S
        RETLW   0x55                ;U
        RETLW   0x52                ;R
        RETLW   0x57                ;W
        RETLW   0x44                ;D
        RETLW   0x4B                ;K
        RETLW   0x47                ;G
        RETLW   0x4F                ;O
```

Listing 14.13: Decode and display routines

length of the previous space. Checks are made by subtracting the required value from the count and seeing if the result has gone negative. Negative numbers have bit seven set, so this is checked by 'AND'ing the number with 0x80 (bit seven set only) and then checking the ZERO bit of the STATUS register.

The MARK routine makes three checks:

- A count of 6 is used to discard glitches caused by noise
- The potentiometer count is used to find inter-bit gaps
- Twice the potentiometer count is used to separate inter-character gaps from inter-word gaps.

The SPACE routine does not need to do this last check as it only has to differentiate dots from dashes.

The Morse character is stored as a series of ones and zeros - one for a dash and zero for a dot. However, there is a need to differentiate between an empty bit in the register and a leading dot or series of dots. Therefore, a count is held of the number of bits in the character.

When a dot or dash is received, the contents of the Morse character register is shifted left by one bit, to leave a space for the bit that has just been received. This is then inserted into bit zero and the length register is incremented by one.

The full routines are slightly more complex in that they contain the option to display the dots and dashes directly. The code for a dash (or minus sign) is hexadecimal 0x2D. This is loaded into the 'W' register and then the write data (WD) routine is called. The dot routine is similar except that is outputs a full stop (0x2E).

Back in the timing routines, where the MARK routine or the LONG routine determines that a character needs to be displayed it calls the DECODE routine.

In order to translate a code from Morse to text, the program calls two nested tables. (Note that the word TABLE or any word starting with TABLE is reserved in MPASM and must not be used in a program. Therefore, this program precedes the word TABLE with an 'X'. The word TABLE can, however, be used with TASM).

The first table looks at the length of the Morse character. This calls the appropriate second table. For example, a code of dot, dot dash would be held in the Morse register as 00000001 with a 'morselen' value of 3. The first table read uses the 'morselen' value. With a 'morselen' of three, this table tells the program to go to table 3. This looks at the Morse character itself. A value of 00000001 (or 1) calls the second entry in this table. (The first entry is for a value of zero). This returns a value of 0x55 to the decode routine, which outputs it to the display by calling the write data 'WD' routine). Hexadecimal 55 is the display code for the letter U, so 'dot dot dash' is displayed as the letter U.

Finally, back in the action routine, the Morse character and length registers are cleared. Then, the space register is again looked at to see whether an additional space needs to be added. If so, one is sent to the display.

Full Listings
The complete program listing for this project can be found in the Appendix, and (together with other useful material) at www.rsgb.org/books /extra/picbasics.htm

References

- *PICmicro Mid-Range MCU Family Reference Manual* (DS33023A) from www.microchip.com
- *16F87X Reference Manual* (DS30292C) from www.microchip.com
- *16F87XA Flash Memory Programming Specification* (DS35889B) from www.microchip.com
- *Application Note AN556* (Implementing a Table Read) from www.microchip.com
- *LM567 Data Sheet* (DS006975) from www.national.com
- Data Sheet for item number N27AZ from www.maplin.co.uk
- 'PIC based Morse Decoder' (*RadCom,* June 1999)
- 'Talking Morse Code Reader' (*RadCom,* June 2001)

15

Using PIC chips in your own projects

As you have seen from this book, PIC chips can be used in numerous command, control and measurement applications. I hope that this book has spurred you on to think of ways that you can use PICs in your own projects. However, I am well aware that there is a big difference between building a project that someone else has designed and working on your own. That is why I have included this section in the book.

Stage 1 is to think about what exactly the PIC will do and here the key message is "how little can each PIC do?" not "how much?". Don't try to cram lots of functions into a single chip. Consider using more than one chip and splitting the functions between them. For example, I designed a 2m FM transceiver that was based on an MC145151 synthesiser chip.

Instead of trying to force everything into one PIC, which would easily have fitted, I used two PICs. One controlled the frequency and the other controlled the display. PIC1 was driven by interrupts whereas PIC2 was on a continuous instruction loop. The end result was that each chip had more than enough time to do it's work without any fear of being overloaded. It also helped with development and fault finding.

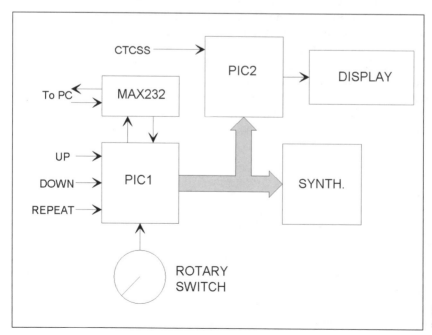

Fig 14.1: PIC based synthesiser control

Chip Type	Pins	Port Pins (Max)	Compa-rators	A/D pins	A/D bits	8 bit Count	16 bit Count	UART	EE-PROM
16F505	14	12	0	0		1	0	No	No
16F506	?	12	0	3	8 bit	1	0	No	No
16F54	18	12	0	0		1	0	No	No
16F57	28	20	0	0		1	0	No	No
16F59	40	32	0	0		1	0	No	No
16F627	18	16	2	0		2	1	Yes	128
16F628	18	16	2	0		2	1	Yes	128
16F630	14	12	1	0		1	1	No	128
16F636	14	12	2	0		1	1	No	256
16F639	?	12	2	0		1	1	No	256
16F648	18	16	2	0		2	1	Yes	256
16F676	14	12	1	8	10 bit	1	1	No	128
16F684	14	12	2	8	10 bit	2	1	No	256
16F685	20	18	2	12	10 bit	2	1	No	256
16F687	20	18	2	12	10 bit	2	1	Yes	256
16F688	14	12	2	8	10 bit	1	1	Yes	256
16F679	20	18	2	12	10 bit	1	1	Yes	256
16F690	20	18	2	12	10 bit	2	1	Yes	256
16F716	18	13	0	4	8 bit	2	1	No	No
16F72	28	22	0	5	8 bit	2	1	No	No
16F73	28	22	0	5	8 bit	2	1	Yes	No
16F737	28	25	2	11	10 bit	2	1	Yes	No
16F74	40	33	0	5	8 bit	2	1	Yes	No
16F747	40	36	2	14	10 bit	2	1	Yes	No
16F76	28	22	0	5	8 bit	2	1	Yes	No
16F767	28	25	2	11	10 bit	2	1	Yes	No
16F77	40	33	0	8	8 bit	2	1	Yes	No
16F777	40	36	2	14	10 bit	2	1	Yes	No
16F785	20	18	2	12	10 bit	2	1	No	256
16F818	18	16	0	5	10 bit	2	1	No	128
16F819	18	16	0	5	10 bit	2	1	No	256
16F84	18	13	0	0		1	0	No	64
16F87	18	16	2	0		2	1	Yes	256
16F870	28	22	0	5	10 bit	2	1	Yes	64
16F871	40	33	0	8	10 bit	2	1	Yes	64
16F872	28	22	2	5	10 bit	2	1	No	64
16F873	28	22	2	5	10 bit	2	1	Yes	128
16F874	40	33	2	8	10 bit	2	1	Yes	128
16F876	28	22	2	5	10 bit	2	1	Yes	256
16F877	40	33	2	8	10 bit	2	1	Yes	256
16F88	18	16	2	7	10 bit	2	1	Yes	256
16F913	28	25	2	5	10 bit	2	1	Yes	256
16F914	40	36	2	8	10 bit	2	1	Yes	256
16F916	28	25	2	5	10 bit	2	1	Yes	256
16F917	40	36	2	8	10 bit	2	1	Yes	256
16F946	64 *	53	2	8	10 bit	2	1	Yes	256

Notes: * With the exception of the 16F946, which is in a square package with 16 pins on each side, the other chips are all available as dual in-line (DIL) chips. All DIL chips up to and including 28 pins have 0.3" spacing between the two rows of pins. 40 pin chips have 0.6" row spacing. It should be noted that 0.3" row spaced chip holders are not readily available for chips with more than 20 pins. However, they can be built from smaller chip holders. For example, two 14 pin holders.

Only reprogrammable types are shown in this chart. Any chip that does not have the letter 'F' in its type number may not be reprogrammable.

Table 15.1: PIC types

Table 15.2: Local oscillator frequencies

Frequency	Step (Decimal)	Hexadecimal	Binary
133,300kHz	10664	29A8	10 1001 1010 1000
135,300kHz	10824	2A48	10 1010 0100 1000

Selecting the chip type

Tables 15.1 and 15.2 should help you choose a chip type. However, it is always worth looking at the chip types that are more readily available to Radio Amateurs. In the UK, one well known company sells only a small selection of these.

For my synthesised 2m FM transceiver, I needed a range of 133.3MHz to 135.3MHz as I had a first IF of 10.7MHz. An extra line into the synthesiser chip raised the frequency by 10.7MHz on transmit so I did not need to cover the transmit frequencies directly. With a channel spacing, and reference frequency, of 12.5kHz, the synthesiser needs to cover from 10664 times to 10824 times the reference frequency. (10664 times 12.5 is 133300 and 10824 times 12.5 is 135300). Table 15.2 shows this in hexadecimal and binary.

From the binary table, it can be seen that the first (left hand) four bits are always '1010' and so this can be hard wired onto the synthesiser chip. This means that I only needed 10 bits of changeable data. You can check this by taking any FM channel, subtracting the IF frequency of 10.7MHz and dividing by 12.5kHz. For example, 145.5875MHz minus 10.7MHz is 134.8875. Divide this by 0.0125MHz gives 10791, which in binary is 10101000100111. As before, the first four bits are 1010.

Then I looked at the other connections to the PIC. These were:
- Rotary encoder (2 lines)
- Up switch
- Down switch
- Repeater on/off switch
- Transmit/repeater reverse switch
- UART for connection to a PC (2 lines)

This meant that I needed at least 18 input/output bits and I needed a PIC with a built-in UART. I didn't need any comparators or A/D converters. A quick check and the 16F73 seemed ideal. It was readily available from the major suppliers in the UK and relatively cheap at about £5 each. Then I saw that the 16F873 also had built-in EEPROM and this got me thinking about building memories for my radio. It had 22 input/output pins so I had some capacity to expand the system by adding memory-save and memory-recall buttons.

For PIC2, I did not need a UART but I did need a chip with lots of input output lines. 10 for the frequency, 11 for the display and 6 for the CTCSS (which I also needed to display). The 16F874 satisfied these conditions as it had 33 input/output lines.

Having selected these chips, a quick check on my programmers showed up a problem. None of my programmers will program a 40 pin chip and the 16F874 has 40 pins. (The 16F873 has only 28 pins). However, the programming manuals showed that the programming algorithm was the same as the 16F873 and so I had the option of building a 16 pin to 40 pin converter out of a 16 pin chip header and a 40 pin socket or using in-circuit programming.

Developing the software

Having got the chips, the next stage was to develop the software. Here, the trick is to take it very slowly. Experience has taught me never to try and design a fully functional program in one go. Therefore, I designed this in a series of iterative steps.

Stage 1 was to build a test rig of DIL switches and pull-up resistors on a small piece of stripboard. This was used to test PIC2. It was also (separately) used to develop the synthesiser hardware as it could be manually switched to any channel. Therefore, the two developments could happen in parallel. My first PIC program merely copied the switch positions onto the screen of the display.

Once I had that, I could start to develop the software for PIC1, with the two PIC programs being developed in parallel but independently of each other. For the display, the first step was to convert the binary code into a frequency. Then I added a message relating to repeater use. I picked up the transmit signal and added a transmit/receive message. After that I added a repeater message. Next came the CTCSS tone letters and frequencies. Finally, I added error messages, startup messages and memory save/recall messages. Several times during the development process, I had to fall back to the last working state and try to work out what was wrong.

For PIC1, I started with just the up and down buttons, ensuring that it did not go beyond the band edges. Then I added the rotary control. Next I added the UART. After that came the repeater shift, ensuring that this could only happen in the repeater parts of the band (145.6 MHz to 145.8 MHz in the UK). A reverse shift came next. Finally, I added the memory functions.

For a project of this size, I found that I needed four of each type of PIC:

- Two to work with. This avoids the need to remove the chip, then erase and reprogram it before testing can continue. It also means that you can compare two iterations of the program.
- One containing the last working version.
- One to experiment with. This allows you to try things that are only concerned with the feature you are trying to introduce and to do it in isolation.

I don't think that any of these iterations worked first time. They all needed fault finding and that is the secret of developing new software for the PIC. Before you start writing any program, ask yourself "how will I know that this is working?" If the answer relies on another feature, then has that other feature been proved to work?

Take, for example, the display PIC (PIC2 in the above example). Everything in this project depended on being able to control the display so my first program simply wrote some static data to the display. It didn't work so I tried to monitor whether the lines were changing. However, because it only outputted a few bytes, I didn't have time to monitor anything before it was over. So I put a loop in the program and suddenly the display burst into life. Conclusion - it must be timing. It was only after very careful reading of the manual for the display that I discovered that it needed a very long switch on delay. After adding it to my program, the display worked and I could move on to the next sub project.

A thinking mind and a logical approach to fault finding are far more important than lots of tools when it comes to developing PIC software. I do have a small oscilloscope but I rarely use it. A digital (high impedance) multi-meter set on AC and with a capacitor in the active lead is usually enough to see whether a signal is pulsing. I don't have lots of other tools either, preferring hand tools and time to power tools. Indeed, my only power tool is a small hobby drill (without a stand) that I use for cutting away the copper on printed circuit boards.

Getting help

My main source of help is the Internet. Microchip have an excellent web site that contains everything you need to know about the PIC itself. For other components, my first stop is usually the supplier or manufacturer's web site. Other web sites that I regularly use are the DataSheet Archive and Maplin's. Failing these, use a search engine and you will normally be pleasantly surprised at how much information they can come up with. The trick is in phrasing the question. Some search engines require you to put numbers inside speech (quotation) marks.

Useful web sites

- Microchip: www.microchip.com
- The DataSheet Archive: www.datasheetarchive.com
- Maplin: www.maplin.co.uk

Other projects

There are many PIC based projects that are published from time to time in magazines such as *QST* and *RadCom*. I have been influenced by many of these. The scope of these projects ranges from very simple to complex projects, such as:

- 'Pic-n-Mix Digital Injection Oscillator', which was described in *RadCom* between January 1999 and May 1999.
- 'PICaTUNE automatic antenna tuning unit', which was originally described in *RadCom* between September 2000 and January 2001. It was subsequently featured in the *RSGB* book 'Command'.
- 'PICaSTAR, a software controlled transmitter and receiver', which was described in *RadCom* between August 2002 and March 2004, and is featured in full in the RSGB *Radio Communication Handbook*.

Appendix - the full listings

his appendix contains full MPASM listings for each of the projects in this book. TASM listings and compiled programs, together with PC programs for those projects that have a PC based element, can be found at www.rsgb.org/books/extra/picbasics.htm.

Full listing for Project 1: A clock for the shack

```
            __config 3ffa

;Clock Program

;PIC Registers
INDR      EQU      0x00
PCL       EQU      0x02
STATUS    EQU      0x03          ;Used for Zero bit
FSR       EQU      0x04
PORTA     EQU      0x05
PORTB     EQU      0x06
PCLATH    EQU      0x0A


;PIC Bits
W         EQU      0
F         EQU      1
ZERO      EQU      2


;Project Registers
HRTWO     EQU      0x10          ;Count 0 - 2. Updated every 10 Hrs. LH disp digit.
HRTEN     EQU      0x11          ;Count 0 - 9. Updated every Hr. 2nd display digit.
MINSIX    EQU      0x12          ;Count 0 - 5. Updated every 10 Min. 3rd disp digit
MINTEN    EQU      0x13          ;Count 0 - 9. Updated every Min. 4th disp digit
LETU      EQU      0x14          ;Letter U. Fifth display digit.
LETT      EQU      0x15          ;Letter T. Sixth display digit.
LETC      EQU      0x16          ;Letter C. Seventh display digit.
BLANK     EQU      0x16          ;Unused eighth display digit.
COUNT     EQU      0x18          ;Count 0 - 200. Updated every 5ms
CNT2      EQU      0x19          ;Count 0 - 5. Updated every 1ms
SECS      EQU      0x1A          ;Count 0 - 59. Updated every 1ms
HOURS     EQU      0x1B          ;Count 0 - 23. Updated every Hour
CHAR      EQU      0x1C          ;Display Digit 0-7
DIGIT     EQU      0x1D          ;PortA Count (0-28 in 4's)
DELAY     EQU      0x1E          ;Delay Count
;Project Bits

;START!!!
```

```
              ORG       5

;Initialise
              BSF       STATUS, 5   ;
              MOVLW     0x03
              MOVWF     PORTA       ;PORTA = Bits 2-5 = Output, 0-1 = Input
              CLRF      PORTB       ;PORTB = Output
              BCF       STATUS, 5   ;
              CLRF      PCLATH
              CLRF      CHAR
              CLRF      DIGIT
              CLRF      COUNT
              CLRF      CNT2
              CLRF      SECS
              MOVLW     0x00
              MOVWF     MINTEN
              MOVLW     0x00
              MOVWF     MINSIX
              MOVLW     0x02
              MOVWF     HRTEN
              MOVLW     0x01
              MOVWF     HRTWO
              MOVLW     0x0C
              MOVWF     HOURS
              MOVLW     0x0A
              MOVWF     LETU
              MOVLW     0x0B
              MOVWF     LETT
              MOVLW     0x0C
              MOVWF     LETC

;Update Display

TICK          MOVLW     0xFF
              MOVWF     PORTB       ;Clear Display

              MOVF      DIGIT, W    ;Update PortA
              ADDLW     0x04
              ANDLW     0x1C
              MOVWF     DIGIT
              MOVWF     PORTA

              INCF      CHAR, W     ;Update character
              ANDLW     0x07
              MOVWF     CHAR
              ADDLW     0x10
              MOVWF     FSR
              MOVF      INDR, W     ;Get char
              ANDLW     0x0F
              CALL      TABLE       ;Returns with display in W
              MOVWF     PORTB

              MOVLW     0xC9
              MOVWF     DELAY
LOOP1         DECFSZ    DELAY, F
              GOTO      LOOP1

              MOVLW     0x79
              MOVWF     DELAY
LOOP2         DECFSZ    DELAY, F
```

```
        GOTO      LOOP2
        NOP                         ;Each NOP adds 1 second per 1000.
        NOP

        INCF      CNT2, F           ;End of 1mS loop
        MOVF      CNT2, W
        SUBLW     0x05
        BTFSS     STATUS, ZERO      ;5mS?
        GOTO      TICK              ;No
        CLRF      CNT2              ;Yes
        NOP                         ;Each NOP adds 1 second per 5000.


        INCF      COUNT, F          ;End of 5mS loop
        MOVF      COUNT, W
        SUBLW     0xC8
        BTFSS     STATUS, ZERO      ;One Second?
        GOTO      TICK              ;No
        CLRF      COUNT             ;Yes
        NOP                         ;Each NOP adds 1 second per 1,000,000.

        BTFSS     PORTA, 0
        GOTO      INCMIN
        BTFSS     PORTA, 1
        GOTO      INCHR

        INCF      SECS, F           ;End of 1 Second loop
        MOVF      SECS, W
        SUBLW     0x3C
        BTFSS     STATUS, ZERO      ;One Minute?
        GOTO      TICK              ;No
        CLRF      SECS              ;Yes
        NOP                         ;Each NOP adds 1 second per 60,000,000.

INCMIN  INCF      MINTEN, F         ;End of 1 Minute loop
        MOVF      MINTEN, W
        SUBLW     0x0A
        BTFSS     STATUS, ZERO      ;Ten Minutes?
        GOTO      TICK              ;No
        CLRF      MINTEN            ;Yes

        INCF      MINSIX, F         ;End of 10 Minute loop
        MOVF      MINSIX, W
        SUBLW     0x06
        BTFSS     STATUS, ZERO      ;One Hour?
        GOTO      TICK              ;No
        CLRF      MINSIX            ;Yes

INCHR   INCF      HOURS, F          ;End of 1 Hour loop
        INCF      HRTEN, F
        MOVF      HRTEN, W
        SUBLW     0x0A
        BTFSS     STATUS, ZERO      ;Ten Hours?
        GOTO      H1                ;No
        CLRF      HRTEN             ;Yes

        INCF      HRTWO, F          ;End of 10 Hour loop
        GOTO      TICK
```

```
H1          MOVF        HOURS, W
            SUBLW       0x18
            BTFSS       STATUS, ZERO   ;24 Hours?
            GOTO        TICK        ;No
            CLRF        HOURS
            CLRF        HRTEN
            CLRF        HRTWO
            GOTO        TICK



TABLE:      ADDWF   PCL, F
            RETLW       0x01         ;Zero
            RETLW       0x57         ;One
            RETLW       0x22         ;Two
            RETLW       0x12         ;Three
            RETLW       0x54         ;Four
            RETLW       0x18         ;Five
            RETLW       0x08         ;Six
            RETLW       0x53         ;Seven
            RETLW       0x00         ;Eight
            RETLW       0x50         ;Nine
            RETLW       0x0F         ;10 = "U"
            RETLW       0x2C         ;11 = "T"
            RETLW       0x2E         ;12 = "C"
            RETLW       0xFF         ;13
            RETLW       0xFF         ;14
            RETLW       0xFF         ;15
            RETLW       0xFF         ;16


            END
```

Full Listing for Project 2: Morse Key

```
            __config 3ff8

;
; Morse Key Program
;

;Defines
#DEFINE REGHI    BSF 3,5
#DEFINE REGLO    BCF 3,5
#DEFINE KEYDN    BSF 5,3
#DEFINE KEYUP    BCF 5,3

;Internal File Assignments
PORTA    EQU     0x05
PORTB    EQU     0x06

;Internal Bit Assignments
W        EQU     0
F        EQU     1

;User File Assignments
TIMER1   EQU     0x10
```

```
        TIMER2  EQU     0x11

        ;User Bit Assignments
        IAMBIC  EQU     1
        DOTKEY  EQU     4
        DASHKEY EQU     3
        KEYOUT  EQU     3

        ;Program Starts Here!!!!!!!!!


                ORG     0x05


                REGHI
                MOVLW   0x03                    ;Set PORTA bits 0,1 to inputs,
                MOVWF   PORTA                   ;bits 2,3,4 to outputs
                MOVLW   0xFF
                MOVWF   PORTB                   ;Set PORTB to all inputs
                REGLO

        LOOP    BTFSS   PORTB, DOTKEY   ;Is Dot Key Pressed
                GOTO    DOT                     ;Yes, go to Dot routine
                BTFSS   PORTB, DASHKEY  ;Is Dash Key Pressed
                GOTO    DASH                            ;Yes, go to Dash routine
                GOTO    LOOP

        DOT     KEYDN
                NOP
                NOP
                NOP
                NOP
                NOP
                NOP
                CALL    TIME
                KEYUP
                CALL    TIME
                BTFSC   PORTB, DOTKEY   ;Is Dot Key Still pressed?
                GOTO    LOOP                    ;No, so go back to loop
                BTFSS   PORTA, IAMBIC   ;Yes - Is Iambic switch set?
                GOTO    DOT                     ;No so do another Dot
                GOTO    DASH                    ;Yes, so do a dash

        DASH    KEYDN
                NOP
                NOP
                NOP
                NOP
                NOP
                NOP
                CALL    TIME
                CALL    TIME
                CALL    TIME
                KEYUP
                CALL    TIME
                BTFSC   PORTB, DASHKEY  ;Is Dash Key Still pressed?
                GOTO    LOOP                    ;No, so go back to loop
                BTFSS   PORTA, IAMBIC   ;Yes - Is Iambic switch set?
                GOTO    DASH                    ;No so do another Dash
                GOTO    DOT                     ;Yes, so do a dot

        TIME    MOVLW   0x16
```

```
                MOVWF      TIMER1
        T1      MOVLW      0x80
                MOVWF      TIMER2
        T2      DECFSZ     TIMER2,F
                GOTO       T2
                DECFSZ     TIMER1,F
                GOTO       T1
                RETURN

                END
```

Full listing for Project 3: Automatic Morse Generator - single message

```
                __config 3ff8

        ;
        ; Single Message Morse Program
        ;

        ;Defines
        #DEFINE  REGHI       BSF 3,5
        #DEFINE  REGLO       BCF 3,5
        #DEFINE  KEYDN       BSF 5,1
        #DEFINE  KEYUP       BCF 5,1

        ;Internal File Assignments
        PCL      EQU         0x02
        PORTA    EQU         0x05
        PORTB    EQU         0x06
        PCLATH   EQU         0x0A

        ;Internal Bit Assignments
        W        EQU         0
        F        EQU         1

        ;User File Assignments
        OFFSET   EQU         0x0D
        TIMER1   EQU         0x10
        TIMER2   EQU         0x11

        ;User Bit Assignments
        KEYIN    EQU         2
        KEYOUT   EQU         1

        ;Program Starts Here!!!!!!!!!

                ORG         5

                CLRF        PORTA
                CLRF        PORTB
                CLRF        PCLATH
                REGHI
                CLRF        PORTA       ;Set PORTA to all outputs
                MOVLW       0xFF
                MOVLW       PORTB       ;Set PORTB to all inputs
                REGLO
```

```
LOOP      BTFSS     PORTB,0         ;Is Switch  pressed
          GOTO      PTABLE          ;Yes
          GOTO      LOOP                   ;No

DOT       KEYDN
          CALL      TIME
          KEYUP
          CALL      TIME
          RETURN

DASH      KEYDN
          CALL      TIME
          CALL      TIME
          CALL      TIME
          KEYUP
          CALL      TIME
          RETURN


PSPACE    CALL      TIME
          CALL      TIME
          CALL      TIME
          RETURN

LONG      CALL      TIME
          CALL      TIME
          CALL      TIME
          CALL      TIME
          CALL      TIME
          RETURN

TIME      MOVLW     0x16
          MOVWF     TIMER1
T1        MOVLW     0x80
          MOVWF     TIMER2
T2        DECFSZ    TIMER2,F
          GOTO      T2
          DECFSZ    TIMER1,F
          GOTO      T1
          RETURN

PEND      GOTO      LOOP

PTABLE    CALL      DOT
          CALL      DASH
          CALL      PSPACE
          CALL      DOT
          CALL      DASH
          CALL      LONG
          GOTO      PEND

          END
```

Full listing for Project 4: Two-tone audio generator

```
            __config 3f79

;Internal File Assignments
PCL       EQU        0x02
PORTB     EQU        0x06
PORTC     EQU        0x07
PCLATH    EQU        0x0A

;Internal Bit Assignments
W         EQU        0
F         EQU        1

;User File Assignments
TIMER     EQU        0x21
STEP      EQU        0x22


;Program Starts Here!!!!!!!!!
                     ORG       0x00
                     GOTO      START
                     NOP
                     NOP
                     NOP
                     NOP
                     NOP
                     NOP
                     NOP
                     NOP
                     NOP
                     NOP


START    BSF         3, 5
                     CLRF      PORTB
                     MOVLW     0xFF
                     MOVWF     PORTC
                     BCF       3, 5
                     MOVLW     0x01
                     MOVWF     STEP




LOOP     CLRF        PCLATH
                     SWAPF     PORTC, W
                     ANDLW     0x07
                     ADDWF     PCL, F
                     GOTO      T0          ;Tone 0 = No Tone
                     GOTO      T1          ;Tone 1 = 800Hz
                     GOTO      T2          ;Tone 2 = 1500Hz
                     GOTO      T3          ;Tone 3 = Two Tone
(800+1500)
                     GOTO      T5          ;Tone 4 = 1kHz
                     GOTO      T5          ;Tone 5 = 300Hz
                     GOTO      T0          ;Tone 6
                     GOTO      T0          ;Tone 7
```

```
T0          MOVLW  0x80                    ;No Tone
            MOVWF  PORTB
            CALL   DELAY
            CALL   DELAY
            GOTO   LOOP


DELAY  MOVLW  0x11                    ;0x11 = 17
            MOVWF  TIMER
D1     DECFSZ TIMER, F                ;17 * 3 = 51
            GOTO   D1
            NOP                                        ;Trimmer NOPs
            NOP
            RETURN


T4          MOVLW  0x00                    ;1kHz Tone
            MOVWF  PCLATH
            MOVLW  0x0C                        ;0x0C = 12
            DECFSZ STEP, F                    ;End of cycle
            GOTO   J4                        ;No
            MOVWF  STEP              ;Yes - reload
J4     CALL   DELAY           ;Wait
            CALL   TA4             ;Get next part of waveform
            MOVWF  PORTB           ;Output to port B
            GOTO   LOOP


TA4    MOVF   STEP, W          ;Get location within cycle
            ADDWF  PCL, F                   ;Add to program counter
            RETLW  0x00
            RETLW  0x80
            RETLW  0xBF
            RETLW  0xEE
            RETLW  0xFF
            RETLW  0xEE
            RETLW  0xC0
            RETLW  0x80
            RETLW  0x40
            RETLW  0x11
            RETLW  0x00
            RETLW  0x11
            RETLW  0x3F


T5          MOVLW  0x00                    ;300kHz Tone
            MOVWF  PCLATH
            MOVLW  0x28                        ;0x28 = 40
            DECFSZ STEP, F
            GOTO   J5
            MOVWF  STEP
J5     CALL   DELAY
            CALL   TA5
            MOVWF  PORTB
            GOTO   LOOP


TA5    MOVF   STEP, W
            ADDWF  PCL, F
            RETLW  0x00
            RETLW  0x80
            RETLW  0x94
```

```
                        RETLW      0xA7
                        RETLW      0xBA
                        RETLW      0xCB
                        RETLW      0xDA
                        RETLW      0xE7
                        RETLW      0xF2
                        RETLW      0xF9
                        RETLW      0xFE
                        RETLW      0xFF
                        RETLW      0xFE
                        RETLW      0xF9
                        RETLW      0xF2
                        RETLW      0xE7
                        RETLW      0xDA
                        RETLW      0xCB
                        RETLW      0xBA
                        RETLW      0xA7
                        RETLW      0x94
                        RETLW      0x80
                        RETLW      0x6B
                        RETLW      0x58
                        RETLW      0x45
                        RETLW      0x34
                        RETLW      0x25
                        RETLW      0x18
                        RETLW      0xD
                        RETLW      0x6
                        RETLW      0x1
                        RETLW      0x0
                        RETLW      0x1
                        RETLW      0x6
                        RETLW      0xD
                        RETLW      0x18
                        RETLW      0x25
                        RETLW      0x34
                        RETLW      0x45
                        RETLW      0x58
                        RETLW      0x6B

T1          MOVLW   0x00                             ;800kHz Tone
                        MOVWF      PCLATH
                        MOVLW      0x0F                  ;0x28 = 15
                        DECFSZ     STEP, F
                        GOTO       J1
                        MOVWF      STEP
J1          CALL    DELAY
                        CALL       TA1
                        MOVWF      PORTB
                        GOTO       LOOP


TA1         MOVF    STEP, W
                        ADDWF      PCL, F
                        RETLW      0x00
                        retlw      0x80
                        retlw      0xB4
                        retlw      0xDF
                        retlw      0xF9
                        retlw      0xFF
                        retlw      0xEE
```

```
                retlw       0xCB
                retlw       0x9A
                retlw       0x65
                retlw       0x34
                retlw       0x11
                retlw       0x0
                retlw       0x6
                retlw       0x20
                retlw       0x4B

T2      MOVLW   0x00                            ;1500kHz Tone
                MOVWF       PCLATH
                MOVLW       0x08
                DECFSZ      STEP, F
                GOTO        J2
                MOVWF       STEP
J2      CALL    DELAY
                CALL        TA2
                MOVWF       PORTB
                GOTO        LOOP


TA2     MOVF    STEP, W
                ADDWF       PCL, F
                retlw       0x00
                retlw       0x80
                retlw       0xDA
                retlw       0xFF
                retlw       0xDA
                retlw       0x80
                retlw       0x25
                retlw       0x0
                retlw       0x25


                ORG         0x100
T3      MOVLW   0x01                            ;Two Tone (800+1500)
                MOVWF       PCLATH
                MOVLW       0x28                    ;0x78 = 120
                DECFSZ      STEP, F
                GOTO        J3
                MOVWF       STEP
J3      CALL    DELAY
                CALL        TA3
                MOVWF       PORTB
                GOTO        LOOP


TA3     MOVF    STEP, W
                ADDWF       PCL, F
                RETLW       0x00
                RETLW       0x80
                RETLW       0xC3
                RETLW       0xEA
                RETLW       0xE5
                RETLW       0xBD
                RETLW       0x89
                RETLW       0x66
                RETLW       0x60
                RETLW       0x72
```

```
RETLW       0x86
RETLW       0x87
RETLW       0x6D
RETLW       0x45
RETLW       0x26
RETLW       0x29
RETLW       0x53
RETLW       0x97
RETLW       0xD8
RETLW       0xF7
RETLW       0xE8
RETLW       0xB5
RETLW       0x78
RETLW       0x4E
RETLW       0x47
RETLW       0x5A
RETLW       0x75
RETLW       0x7F
RETLW       0x70
RETLW       0x52
RETLW       0x3B
RETLW       0x41
RETLW       0x6C
RETLW       0xAC
RETLW       0xE5
RETLW       0xFA
RETLW       0xE0
RETLW       0xA4
RETLW       0x60
RETLW       0x35
RETLW       0x2F
RETLW       0x49
RETLW       0x6D
RETLW       0x82
RETLW       0x7D
RETLW       0x67
RETLW       0x53
RETLW       0x5A
RETLW       0x81
RETLW       0xB9
RETLW       0xE8
RETLW       0xF2
RETLW       0xCF
RETLW       0x8C
RETLW       0x47
RETLW       0x1D
RETLW       0x1E
RETLW       0x41
RETLW       0x70
RETLW       0x8F
RETLW       0x92
RETLW       0x7F
RETLW       0x6C
RETLW       0x6F
RETLW       0x8E
RETLW       0xBC
RETLW       0xE0
RETLW       0xE1
RETLW       0xB7
RETLW       0x73
```

```
RETLW     0x2F
RETLW     0xC
RETLW     0x16
RETLW     0x44
RETLW     0x7D
RETLW     0xA4
RETLW     0xAA
RETLW     0x98
RETLW     0x81
RETLW     0x7C
RETLW     0x91
RETLW     0xB4
RETLW     0xCF
RETLW     0xC9
RETLW     0x9E
RETLW     0x5B
RETLW     0x1E
RETLW     0x4
RETLW     0x19
RETLW     0x51
RETLW     0x92
RETLW     0xBC
RETLW     0xC3
RETLW     0xAD
RETLW     0x8E
RETLW     0x7F
RETLW     0x89
RETLW     0xA3
RETLW     0xB7
RETLW     0xB0
RETLW     0x86
RETLW     0x4A
RETLW     0x16
RETLW     0x7
RETLW     0x26
RETLW     0x66
RETLW     0xAA
RETLW     0xD5
RETLW     0xD8
RETLW     0xBA
RETLW     0x91
RETLW     0x77
RETLW     0x78
RETLW     0x8B
RETLW     0x9E
RETLW     0x98
RETLW     0x75
RETLW     0x42
RETLW     0x19
RETLW     0x14
RETLW     0x3B


END
```

Full listing for Project 5: 30MHz frequency counter

```
          __config 3f79

;Long (100ms) Count
;
;Display (0-6) connected to RA0 thru RA2
;Digit   (0-9) connected to RC4 thru RC7
;Gate is RC3
;Reset 74HC4040 is RC2
;Count In is RC0
;74HC4040 data is RB0-7
;

;Definitions

;PIC Registers
INDR      EQU      0
PCL       EQU      2
STATUS    EQU      3            ;Used for Zero bit
FSR       EQU      4
PORTA     EQU      5
PORTB     EQU      6
PORTC     EQU      7
PCLATH    EQU      0x0A         ;Program Counter High Bits
INTCON    EQU      0x0B         ;Interrupt Control
TMR1L     EQU      0x0E         ;Least Significant Byte of Counter
TMR1H     EQU      0x0F         ;Most Significant Byte of Counter
T1CON     EQU      0x10         ;Counter Control

;PIC Bits
W         EQU      0
F         EQU      1
CARRY     EQU      0
ZERO      EQU      2


TMR1ON    EQU      0
TMR1CS    EQU      1
T1SYNC    EQU      2
T1OSCEN   EQU      3
T1CKPS0   EQU      4
T1CKPS1   EQU      5


;Project Registers
D7        EQU      0x20
D6        EQU      0x21
D5        EQU      0x22
D4        EQU      0x23
D3        EQU      0x24
D2        EQU      0x25
D1        EQU      0x26
D0        EQU      0x27
DIGIT     EQU      0x28
CHAR      EQU      0x29
LOOP      EQU      0x2A
DELAY     EQU      0x2B
LCOUNT    EQU      0x2C


HDATA     EQU      0x32
```

```
HTEMP      EQU        0x33
HCARRY     EQU        0x34
HOFFSET    EQU        0x35
HOFFBIT    EQU        0x36


;Project Bits
GATE       EQU        3
RST        EQU        2


;START!!!
           ORG        0x10


;Initialise
           BSF        3, 5
           BCF        3, 6        ;
           CLRF       PORTA    ;PORTA = Output
           MOVLW      0xFF
           MOVWF      PORTB    ;PORTB = Input
           MOVLW      0x03
           MOVWF      PORTC    ;PORTC = (0-1=Input) (2-7=Output)
           BCF        3, 5
           CLRF       PCLATH
           CLRF       DIGIT
           CLRF       D0
           CLRF       D1
           CLRF       D2
           CLRF       D3
           CLRF       D4
           CLRF       D5
           CLRF       D6
           CLRF       D7
           CLRF       T1CON
           BSF        T1CON, T1OSCEN
           BSF        T1CON, TMR1CS
           BCF        PORTC, GATE


;Set Up Count
LONG           MOVLW        0x64
           MOVWF      LCOUNT


;Reset Counters etc
           CLRF       DIGIT
           BSF         PORTC, RST
           CLRF       TMR1L
           CLRF       TMR1H
           BCF        PORTC, RST


;Open Gates
           BSF        T1CON, TMR1ON
           BSF        PORTC, GATE


;Main Delay Loop
WAIT       CALL       TICK
           DECFSZ     LCOUNT, F
           GOTO       WAIT
           MOVLW      0x1E
           MOVWF      DELAY
SHORT      DECFSZ     DELAY, F
           GOTO       SHORT
```

```
        ;Close Gate
                BCF         PORTC, GATE
                BCF         T1CON, TMR1ON


        ;Loop to end of cycle
                MOVLW       0x03
                MOVWF       LCOUNT
        WAIT2   CALL        TICK
                DECFSZ      LCOUNT, F
                GOTO        WAIT2


        ;Decode display
                CLRF        D0
                CLRF        D1
                CLRF        D2
                CLRF        D3
                CLRF        D4
                CLRF        D5
                CLRF        D6
                CLRF        D7
                MOVF        TMR1H, W
                MOVWF       HDATA
                CALL        HEX2BCD
                MOVF        TMR1L, W
                MOVWF       HDATA
                CALL        HEX2BCD
                MOVF        PORTB, W
                MOVWF       HDATA
                CALL        HEX2BCD
                CALL        BLANK
                GOTO        LONG



        ;Output Digit (16uS)

        TICK    MOVF        PORTC, W
                IORLW       0xF0
                MOVWF       PORTC       ;Clear Display

                INCF        DIGIT, W    ;Update character
                ANDLW       0x07
                MOVWF       DIGIT
                MOVWF       PORTA
                ADDLW       0x20            ;Register Offset
                MOVWF       FSR
                SWAPF       INDR,  W    ;Get char
                ANDLW       0xF0
                MOVWF       CHAR
                MOVF        PORTC, W
                ANDLW       0x0C
                IORWF       CHAR, W
                MOVWF       PORTC

        ;Delay loop
                MOVLW       0xC8
                MOVWF       DELAY
        LOOP1   DECFSZ      DELAY, F
                GOTO        LOOP1
                NOP                         ;602uS in Loop1
```

```
              MOVLW     0x7C
              MOVWF     DELAY
LOOP2   DECFSZ    DELAY, F
        GOTO      LOOP2
        NOP                        ;392uS in Loop2


        RETURN

;HEX 2 BCD
;Registers used are HDATA, HTEMP, HCARRY, HOFFSET, HOFFBIT
;Digits are in registers 32 - 39
;This routine converts full bytes only.
;Before calling this routine, HDATA must contain data byte to be converted


HEX2BCD            CLRF      HTEMP
        CLRF      HOFFBIT

HLOOP   CLRF      HCARRY
        CLRF      HOFFSET
        BTFSC     HDATA, 7        ;Is bit 7 set?
        INCF      HCARRY, F       ;Yes so set HCARRY

HNXTDGT MOVF      HOFFSET, W      ;Next Digit
        ADDLW     0x20
        MOVWF     FSR

        BCF       STATUS, CARRY ;Clear carry bit
        RLF       INDR, F         ;Multiply data by two
        BTFSC     HCARRY, 0
        INCF      INDR, F
        MOVF      INDR, W
        ADDLW     0x06            ;Add 6
        MOVWF     HTEMP
        CLRF      HCARRY          ;Prepare by clearing HCARRY
        BTFSS     HTEMP, 4        ;Is data > 10? (HTEMP > 16?)
        GOTO      HINCOFF         ;No
        INCF      HCARRY, F       ;Yes so set HCARRY & subtract 10
        MOVLW     0x0A
        SUBWF     INDR, F

HINCOFF INCF      HOFFSET, F      ;Increment offset
        MOVLW     0x07
        SUBWF     HOFFSET, W
        BTFSS     STATUS, ZERO    ;Is it past last digit
        GOTO      HNXTDGT         ;No so do next digit

HNXTBIT INCF      HOFFBIT, F      ;Yes so do next bit
        MOVLW     0x08
        SUBWF     HOFFBIT, W
        BTFSC     STATUS, ZERO    ;Is it past last bit
        RETURN                    ;Yes,all done so return
        RLF       HDATA, F        ;No so shift data
        GOTO      HLOOP

BLANK   MOVF      D1, F
        BTFSS     STATUS, ZERO
        RETURN
        MOVLW     0x0F
        MOVWF     D1
        MOVF      D2, F
```

```
            BTFSS       STATUS, ZERO
            RETURN
            MOVLW       0x0F
            MOVWF       D2
            MOVF        D3, F
            BTFSS       STATUS, ZERO
            RETURN
            MOVLW       0x0F
            MOVWF       D3
            MOVF        D4, F
            BTFSS       STATUS, ZERO
            RETURN
            MOVLW       0x0F
            MOVWF       D4
            RETURN


            END
```

Full listing for Project 6: Digital voltmeter

```
            __config 3f79

;PIC Registers
INDR        EQU         0x00
PCL         EQU         0x02
STATUS      EQU         0x03            ;Used for Zero bit
FSR         EQU         0x04
PORTA       EQU         0x05
PORTB       EQU         0x06
PORTC       EQU         0x07
PCLATH      EQU         0x0A            ;Program Counter High Bits
ADRES       EQU         0x1E            ;A/D Results (Data)
ADCON       EQU         0x1F            ;A/D Converter control

;PIC Bits
W           EQU         0
F           EQU         1
CARRY       EQU         0
ZERO        EQU         2
GO          EQU         2


;Project Registers
D7          EQU         0x20
D6          EQU         0x21
D5          EQU         0x22
D4          EQU         0x23
D3          EQU         0x24
D2          EQU         0x25
D1          EQU         0x26
D0          EQU         0x27
DIGIT       EQU         0x28
COUNT       EQU         0x2B
BINH        EQU         0x2D
BINL        EQU         0x2E
```

```
HDATA       EQU         0x30
HTEMP       EQU         0x31
HCARRY      EQU         0x32
HOFFSET     EQU         0x33
HOFFBIT     EQU         0x34


;Program Start

            ORG         0x00
            GOTO        START
            NOP
            NOP
            NOP
            NOP
            NOP
            NOP
            NOP
            NOP
            NOP
;Initialise
START       BSF         3, 5        ;Go to register bank 1
            MOVLW       0x0F        ;Set Port A bits 0-3 In, 4-7 Out
            MOVWF       PORTA
            CLRF        PORTB       ;Set Port B to all outputs
            MOVLW       0x0F        ;Set Port C bits 0-3 In, 4-7 Out
            MOVWF       PORTC
            MOVLW       0x85        ;Right justify, ext Vref, A0+A1 only
            MOVWF       ADCON
            BCF         3, 5
            MOVLW       0x40
            MOVWF       ADCON
            CLRF        PCLATH
            CLRF        DIGIT
            CLRF        D0
            CLRF        D1
            CLRF        D2
            CLRF        D3
            CLRF        D4
            CLRF        D5
            CLRF        D6
            CLRF        D7
            BSF         ADCON, 0    ;Switch A/D on
            CALL        DELAY


;Start of main loop
LOOP        BSF         ADCON, GO   ;Start A/D
            CALL        DELAY       ;Wait at least 9 x 8 = 72us

AD          BTFSC       ADCON, GO
            GOTO        AD

            MOVF        ADRES, W
            MOVWF       BINH


;Over/Under volt detection
            BSF         PORTA, 4    ;Switch off undervolts
            BSF         PORTA, 5    ;Switch off overvolts
            BTFSS       BINH, 0     ;Bit 0 set?
            GOTO        ISLOW       ;No (could be 00)
            BTFSC       BINH, 1     ;Bit 1 set?
```

```
            GOTO      NEXT            ;Yes, so OK
            BCF       PORTA, 4        ;Switch on undervolts
            GOTO      NEXT
ISLOW       BTFSS     BINH, 1         ;Bit 1 set?
            GOTO      NEXT            ;No, so OK
            BCF       PORTA, 5        ;Switch on overvolts

;Get Low byte of conversion
NEXT        BSF       3, 5            ;Go to register bank 1
            MOVF      ADRES, W
            BCF       3, 5            ;Go to register bank 0
            MOVWF     BINL

            CLRF      HTEMP
            ADDLW     0x00            ;Clear carry bit
            RRF       BINH, F
            RRF       BINL, F

;Bin now in 10mV steps
;Add 11 volts (1100 x 10mV) = 0x44C

            CLRF      HTEMP
            ADDLW     0x00            ;Clear carry bit
            MOVLW     0x4C
            ADDWF     BINL, F
            BTFSC     STATUS, CARRY
            INCF      BINH, F
            MOVLW     0x04
            ADDWF     BINH, F

;Convert to BCD

            CLRF      D0
            CLRF      D1
            CLRF      D2
            CLRF      D3
            CLRF      D4
            CLRF      D5
            CLRF      D6
            CLRF      D7
            MOVF      BINH, W
            MOVWF     HDATA
            CALL      HEX2BCD
            MOVF      BINL, W
            MOVWF     HDATA
            CALL      HEX2BCD

;Output next digit
TICK        MOVLW     0xFF
            MOVWF     PORTB
            INCF      DIGIT, W    ;Update digit number
            ANDLW     0x07
            MOVWF     DIGIT
            SWAPF     DIGIT, W
            MOVWF     PORTC
            MOVF      DIGIT, W
            ADDLW     0x20        ;Add Register Offset
            MOVWF     FSR
            NOP
            NOP
```

```
              MOVF       INDR,  W     ;Get Digit
              ANDLW      0x0F
              CALL       TABLE
              MOVWF      PORTB
              CALL       DELAY
              GOTO       LOOP


;HEX 2 BCD
;Registers used are HDATA, HTEMP, HCARRY, HOFFSET, HOFFBIT
;Digits are in registers 32 - 39
;This routine converts full bytes only.
;Before calling this routine, HDATA must contain data byte to be converted

HEX2BCD            CLRF       HTEMP
           CLRF       HOFFBIT

HLOOP      CLRF       HCARRY
           CLRF       HOFFSET
           BTFSC      HDATA, 7          ;Is bit 7 set?
           INCF       HCARRY, F         ;Yes so set HCARRY

HNXTDGT    MOVF       HOFFSET, W  ;Next Digit
           ADDLW      0x20
           MOVWF      FSR
           NOP
           NOP
           CLRF       HTEMP
           ADDLW      0x00              ;Clear carry bit
           RLF        INDR, F           ;Multiply data by two
           MOVF       HCARRY, F         ;Is carry set
           BTFSS      STATUS, ZERO
           INCF       INDR, F
           MOVF       INDR, W
           ADDLW      0x06              ;Add 6
           MOVWF      HTEMP
           CLRF       HCARRY            ;Prepare by clearing HCARRY
           BTFSS      HTEMP, 4          ;Is data > 10? (HTEMP > 16?)
           GOTO       HINCOFF           ;No
           MOVLW      0x01
           MOVWF      HCARRY            ;Yes so set HCARRY & subtract 10
           MOVLW      0x0A
           SUBWF      INDR, F

HINCOFF    INCF       HOFFSET, F  ;Increment offset
           MOVLW      0x07
           SUBWF      HOFFSET, W
           BTFSS      STATUS, ZERO      ;Is it past last digit
           GOTO       HNXTDGT           ;No so do next digit

HNXTBIT    INCF       HOFFBIT, F  ;Yes so do next bit
           MOVLW      0x08
           SUBWF      HOFFBIT, W
           BTFSC      STATUS, ZERO      ;Is it past last bit
           RETURN                       ;Yes,all done so return
           RLF        HDATA, F          ;No so shift data
           GOTO       HLOOP

DELAY      MOVLW      0x80              ;Approx 400us
           MOVWF      COUNT
```

```
DC          DECFSZ      COUNT, F
            GOTO        DC
            RETURN

TABLE       ADDWF       PCL, F
            RETLW       0x09        ;Zero
            RETLW       0xED        ;One
            RETLW       0x43        ;Two
            RETLW       0xC1        ;Three
            RETLW       0xA5        ;Four
            RETLW       0x91        ;Five
            RETLW       0x31        ;Six
            RETLW       0xCD        ;Seven
            RETLW       0x01        ;Eight
            RETLW       0x85        ;Nine
            RETLW       0xFE        ;10
            RETLW       0xFE        ;11
            RETLW       0xFE        ;12
            RETLW       0xFE        ;13
            RETLW       0xFE        ;14
            RETLW       0xFE        ;15
            RETLW       0xFE        ;16


            END
```

Full listing for project 7: A PC-based audio recorder

```
        __config 3f79

; Program RecPIC
;
; This program uses the Analogue to Digital Convertor to generate
; 8000, 8 bit samples per second. It sends these via a 115,200bps
; serial port link to a PC. The companion program "RecPIC.exe" will
; convert these samples to a ".au" file. This file can then be played
; via Windows Media Player.
;
; The PIC used is a 16F73.
; Loop length for 8000 samples/sec (125us) and 20MHz Xtal
; (0.2uS per instruction) is 625 Instructions
;

;Internal File Assignments
STATUS      EQU         0x03        ;Used for Zero bit
PORTA       EQU         0x05
PORTB       EQU         0x06
PORTC       EQU         0x07
TXSTA       EQU         0x18
SPBRG       EQU         0x19
RCSTA       EQU         0x18
TXREG       EQU         0x19
ADRES       EQU         0x1E
ADCON       EQU         0x1F

;Internal Bit Assignments
```

```
W       EQU     0
F       EQU     1
GO      EQU     2
ZERO    EQU     2


;User File Assignments
TIMER1  EQU     0x21
COUNT   EQU     0x22
TEMP    EQU     0x23



;User Bit Assignments
GREEN     EQU     2
RED       EQU     3

;Program Starts Here!!!!!!!!!
        ORG     0x10

;Initialise Registers
        BSF     3, 5
        BCF     3, 6
        MOVLW   0xC0
        MOVWF   PORTC           ;PORTC = Output except UART
        CLRF    PORTB           ;PORTB = Output
        MOVLW   0xFF
        MOVWF   PORTA           ;PORTA = Input

        MOVLW   0x0A
        MOVWF   SPBRG           ;Set Baud Rate to 115200
        BSF     TXSTA, 2        ;Set Baud Rate to High
        BCF     TXSTA, 4        ;Set Async operation
        BCF     3, 5
        BSF     RCSTA, 7
        BSF     3, 5
        BSF     TXSTA, 5

        MOVLW   0x04
        MOVWF   ADCON
        BCF     3, 5
        MOVLW   0x80
        MOVWF   ADCON
        BSF     ADCON, 0

        CLRF    COUNT

;Time Loop (625 instructions total)
LOOP    MOVLW   0x10
        MOVWF   TIMER1
T0      DECFSZ  TIMER1, F
        GOTO    T0

        BSF     ADCON, GO
        NOP                     ;Trimmer NOPs
        NOP
        NOP
        NOP
        NOP
        NOP
        NOP
```

```
                NOP
                MOVLW      0x0C
                MOVWF      PORTC

                 MOVLW     0xBB              ;BC+10=CC = 201*3 = 603+22=625
                MOVWF      TIMER1
        T1      DECFSZ     TIMER1, F
                GOTO       T1
                MOVF       ADRES, W
                MOVWF      TXREG

                IORLW      0x0F
                ADDLW      0x01
                BTFSC      STATUS, ZERO
                BCF        PORTC, RED
                ADDLW      0x10
                BTFSC      STATUS, ZERO
                BCF        PORTC, GREEN

                GOTO       LOOP

                END
```

Full Listing for Project 8: Morse decoder

```
                __config 3f79


        ;PIC Registers
        PCL        EQU      0x02       ;Program Counter low byte
        STATUS     EQU      0x03       ;Used for Zero and Carry bits
        PORTA      EQU      0x05       ;Inputs from PLL, A/D and Switch
        PORTB      EQU      0x06       ;Data output to display
        PORTC      EQU      0x07       ;Control signals to display
        PCLATH     EQU      0x0A       ;Program Counter high byte
        ADRES      EQU      0x1E       ;A/D data register
        ADCON      EQU      0x1F       ;A/D control, register

        ;User Defined Registers
        MARKREG EQU         0x20       ;Dot/Dash signal
        SPACEREG EQU        0x21       ;Space between dots/dashes
        MORSE      EQU       0x24       ;Character
        MORSELEN EQU        0x25       ;Quantity of dots/dashes
        SPEED      EQU       0x28       ;From potentiometer setting
        T1         EQU       0x2C       ;Part of delay loop
        T2         EQU       0x2D       ;Part of delay loop

        ;PIC Bits
        W          EQU       0
        F          EQU       1
        ZERO       EQU       2
        CARRY      EQU       0
        ADON       EQU       0          ;Switches A/D converter on
        GO         EQU       2          ;Starts A/D conversion

        ;User Defined Bits
        ENABLE     EQU       7          ;Strobe to display
```

```
RW       EQU      6              ;Read/Write to display
DC       EQU      5              ;Data/Command to display
INPUT    EQU      2              ;Input from PLL
SWITCH   EQU      4              ;Character/dot-dash switch

;Initialise Ports

              ORG        0x00

         GOTO     START
         NOP
         NOP
         NOP
         NOP
         NOP
         NOP
         NOP
         NOP
         NOP
         NOP
         NOP
         NOP
         NOP
         NOP
         NOP

START    BSF      3, 5           ;Switch to register bank 1
         MOVLW    0xFF
         MOVWF    PORTA          ;Set Port A to all inputs
         CLRF     PORTB          ;Set Port B to all outputs
         CLRF     PORTC          ;Set Port C to all outputs

;Initialise A/D convertor

         MOVLW    0x04           ;Analogue on bits 0 & 1 of port A plus
         MOVWF    ADCON          ;internal voltage referance
         BCF      3, 5           ;Switch to register bank 0
         MOVLW    0x40           ;Set A/D input on bit 0 plus
         MOVWF    ADCON          ;Left justify (8 bit) conversion
         BSF      ADCON, 0       ;Start A/D converter

;Initialise Display

         MOVLW    0x28           ;Initial delay (40mS)
         MOVWF    T2
I2       CALL     DELAY
         DECFSZ   T2, F
         GOTO     I2
         MOVLW    0x30           ;Function Set (8 bit I/F, 1 line)
         CALL     WC
         CALL     DELAY
         MOVLW    0x0F           ;Display On
         CALL     WC
         CALL     DELAY
         MOVLW    0x01           ;Clear Display
         CALL     WC
         CALL     DELAY
         CALL     DELAY
         CALL     DELAY
         MOVLW    0x07           ;Entry Mode (Scrolling from right)
```

```
            CALL        WC
            CALL        DELAY
            MOVLW       0x8F                ;Set Cursor Position (to right edge)
            CALL        WC
            CALL        DELAY

;Display initial text

            MOVLW       0x43                ;Letter C
            CALL        WD
            CALL        DELAY
            MOVLW       0x57                ;Letter W
            CALL        WD
            CALL        DELAY
            MOVLW       0x20                ;Space
            CALL        WD
            CALL        DELAY
            MOVLW       0x44                ;Letter D
            CALL        WD
            CALL        DELAY
            MOVLW       0x65                ;Letter e
            CALL        WD
            CALL        DELAY
            MOVLW       0x63                ;Letter c
            CALL        WD
            CALL        DELAY
            MOVLW       0x6F                ;Letter o
            CALL        WD
            CALL        DELAY
            MOVLW       0x64                ;Letter d
            CALL        WD
            CALL        DELAY
            MOVLW       0x65                ;Letter e
            CALL        WD
            CALL        DELAY
            MOVLW       0x72                ;Letter r
            CALL        WD
            CALL        DELAY
            MOVLW       0x20                ;Space
            CALL        WD
            CALL        DELAY
            MOVLW       0x20                ;Space
            CALL        WD
            CALL        DELAY

;Clear other registers

            CLRF        MORSE
            CLRF        MORSELEN
            CLRF        SPACEREG

;Monitor input line

SP1         BTFSS       PORTA, INPUT        ;Check input line. It signal present?
            GOTO        MARK                ;Yes, so go to mark routine
            INCF        SPACEREG, F         ;No so count length of space
            BTFSC       SPACEREG, 7         ;Is space very long?
            GOTO        LONG                ;Yes, so go to long routine
            CALL        DELAY               ;No so wait a bit longer
            CALL        DELAY
```

```
               CALL      DELAY
               GOTO      SP1               ;Loop

    MARK       CLRF      MARKREG           ;Clear the space count register
               MOVLW     0x06              ;Check length of space count register
               SUBWF     SPACEREG, W       ;First, check if very short
               ANDLW     0x80
               BTFSS     STATUS, ZERO
               GOTO      MK1               ;Too short = glitch
               GOTO      ACTION

    MK1        BTFSC     PORTA, INPUT      ;Check input line. It signal present?
               GOTO      SPCE              ;No, so go to space routine
               INCF      MARKREG, F        ;No so count length of mark
               MOVLW     0x7F              ;Load W register with 127
               BTFSC     MARKREG, 7        ;Check if markreg contains 128 or more
               MOVWF     MARKREG           ;Yes, so load with 127
               CALL      DELAY             ;(No) Wait a bit longer
               CALL      DELAY
               CALL      DELAY
               GOTO      MK1               ;Loop

    SPCE       CLRF      SPACEREG          ;Clear the space count register
               MOVLW     0x06              ;Check length of mark count register
               SUBWF     MARKREG, W        ;First, check if very short
               ANDLW     0x80
               BTFSS     STATUS, ZERO
               GOTO      SP1               ;Too short = glitch
               GOTO      DOTDASH

;OK, so must be dot or dash

    DOTDASH    INCF      MORSELEN, F       ;Increment character length
               MOVF      SPEED, W          ;Get potentiometer value
               SUBWF     MARKREG, W        ;Subtract from mark count
               ANDLW     0x80              ;Get positive/negative bit
               BTFSS     STATUS, ZERO      ;Positive = Dot. Negative = Dash
               GOTO      DOT               ;Dot
               GOTO      DASH              ;Dash

    DASH       RLF       MORSE, F          ;Move morse character one bit left
               BSF       MORSE, 0          ;Set bottom bit
               BTFSS     PORTA, SWITCH     ;Get switch state
               GOTO      SP1               ;Character mode - so go to SP1
               MOVLW     0x2D              ;Dot/dash mode so create dash
               CALL      WD                ;Send to Display
               CLRF      MORSE             ;Delete morse character
               CLRF      MORSELEN
               GOTO      SP1               ;Continue waiting for an edge

    DOT        RLF       MORSE, F          ;Move morse character one bit left
               BCF       MORSE, 0          ;Clear bottom bit
               BTFSS     PORTA, SWITCH     ;Get switch state
               GOTO      SP1               ;Character mode - so go to SP1
               MOVLW     0x2E              ;Dot/dash mode so create dot
               CALL      WD                ;Send to Display
               CLRF      MORSE             ;Delete morse character
               CLRF      MORSELEN
               GOTO      SP1               ;Continue waiting for an edge
```

```
        LONG    MOVF    MORSELEN, F     ;Move reg so zero bit can be tested
                BTFSC   STATUS, ZERO    ;Check is Morselen is zero
                GOTO    L2              ;Yes, no character waiting
                CALL    DECODE          ;No, character waiting
                MOVLW   0x20            ;Load space character
                CALL    WD              ;Write space to display
                CLRF    MORSE           ;Clear character
                CLRF    MORSELEN        ;Zeroise length
        L2      MOVLW   0x7F            ;Load spacereg with 128
                MOVWF   SPACEREG
                GOTO    SP1             ;Continue waiting for an edge

;Action Routine - end of a space
        ACTION  MOVF    SPEED, W        ;Get potentiometer value
                SUBWF   SPACEREG, F     ;Subtract from space count
                MOVF    SPACEREG, W
                ANDLW   0x80            ;Get positive/negative bit
                BTFSS   STATUS, ZERO    ;Test
                GOTO    MK1             ;Short = inter-bit gap (ignore)
                CALL    DECODE          ;Long so decode character
                MOVF    SPEED, W        ;Get potentiometer value (again)
                CLRF    MORSE           ;Clear morse character
                CLRF    MORSELEN
                SUBWF   SPACEREG, W     ;Subtract from space count (again)
                ANDLW   0x80            ;Get positive/negative bit
                BTFSS   STATUS, ZERO    ;Test
                GOTO    MK1             ;Short = inter-character gap (no more to do)
                MOVLW   0x20            ;Long = Inter word gap
                CALL    WD              ;Write space character to display
                GOTO    MK1

;Decode morse character and display it

        DECODE  CALL    XTABLE          ;Call translate tables
                MOVWF   MORSE           ;Is it a character
                MOVF    MORSE, F
                BTFSC   STATUS, ZERO    ;Check if zero
                GOTO    OUT1            ;Bad character do go to out1
                MOVF    MORSE, W         ;Good character
                CALL    WD              ;Write data to display
        OUT1    CLRF    MORSE           ;Clear character
                CLRF    MORSELEN        ;Zeroise length
                        RETURN

;Delay routine (includes read of potentiometer)

        DELAY   MOVLW   0xA6            ;166 (x 3) = 498us (A/D settling time)
                MOVWF   T1
        D1      DECFSZ  T1, F
                GOTO    D1
                BSF     ADCON, GO       ;Start A/D conversion
                MOVLW   0xA5            ;165 (x 3) = 485us (A/D convert time)
                MOVWF   T1
        D2      DECFSZ  T1, F
                GOTO    D2
                RRF     ADRES, W        ;Read and shift A/D result
                MOVWF   SPEED           ;Write to speed register
                RRF     SPEED, F        ;Shift another bit
                MOVLW   0x3F            ;Reduce to 6 bits
                ANDWF   SPEED, F
```

```
                MOVLW       0x0C            ;Add 12 (Speed = 12 to 76)
                ADDWF       SPEED, F        ;Store in speed register
                RETURN

;Write command routine

WC              MOVWF       PORTB
                MOVLW       0x00
                MOVWF       PORTC
                BSF         PORTC, ENABLE
                NOP
                BCF         PORTC, ENABLE
                BSF         PORTC, RW
                RETURN

;Write data routine

WD              MOVWF       PORTB           ;Data/Command to port B
                MOVLW       0x20            ;Set Data/Command line
                MOVWF       PORTC
                BSF         PORTC, ENABLE   ;Set Enable/Strobe bit
                NOP
                BCF         PORTC, ENABLE   ;Remove Enable/Strobe bit
                BSF         PORTC, RW       ;Set read mode
                ETURN


;Translation tables

                ORG         0x100           ;Place program at address 0x100
XTABLE          MOVLW       0x01            ;Set high program counter
                MOVWF       PCLATH
                MOVF        MORSELEN, W     ;Get character length
                ANDLW       0x07            ;Max 7 dot/dash combinations
                ADDWF       PCL, F          ;Add to program counter
                RETLW       0x00            ;No dot/dash
                GOTO        XTABLE1         ;One dot or dash
                GOTO        XTABLE2         ;Two dot/dashes
                GOTO        XTABLE3         ;Three dot/dashes
                GOTO        XTABLE4         ;Four dot/dashes
                GOTO        XTABLE5         ;Five dot/dashes
                GOTO        XTABLE6         ;Six dot/dashes
                RETLW  .    0x00            ;Seven dot/dashes = error

XTABLE1         MOVF        MORSE, W
                ANDLW       0x01
                ADDWF       PCL, F
                RETLW       0x45            ;E
                RETLW       0x54            ;T

XTABLE2         MOVF        MORSE, W
                ANDLW       0x03
                ADDWF       PCL, F
                RETLW       0x49            ;I
                RETLW       0x41            ;A
                RETLW       0x4E            ;N
                RETLW       0x4D            ;M

XTABLE3         MOVF        MORSE, W
                ANDLW       0x07
```

```
          ADDWF     PCL, F
          RETLW     0x53              ;S
          RETLW     0x55              ;U
          RETLW     0x52              ;R
          RETLW     0x57              ;W
          RETLW     0x44              ;D
          RETLW     0x4B              ;K
          RETLW     0x47              ;G
          RETLW     0x4F              ;O

XTABLE4   MOVF      MORSE, W
          ANDLW     0x0F
          ADDWF     PCL, F
          RETLW     0x48              ;H
          RETLW     0x56              ;V
          RETLW     0x46              ;F
          RETLW     0xFF              ;..--
          RETLW     0x4C              ;L
          RETLW     0xFF              ;.-.-
          RETLW     0x50              ;P
          RETLW     0x4A              ;J
          RETLW     0x42              ;B
          RETLW     0x58              ;X
          RETLW     0x43              ;C
          RETLW     0x59              ;Y
          RETLW     0x5A              ;Z
          RETLW     0x51              ;Q
          RETLW     0xFF              ;---.
          RETLW     0xFF              ;----

XTABLE5   MOVF      MORSE, W
          ANDLW     0x1F
          ADDWF     PCL, F
          RETLW     0x35              ;5
          RETLW     0x34              ;4
          RETLW     0xFF              ;...-.
          RETLW     0x33              ;3
          RETLW     0xFF              ;..-..
          RETLW     0xFF              ;..-.-
          RETLW     0xFF              ;..--.
          RETLW     0x32              ;2
          RETLW     0x3D              ;WAIT (=)
          RETLW     0xFF              ;.-..-
          RETLW     0x7F              ;EOM (<-)
          RETLW     0xFF              ;.-.--
          RETLW     0xFF              ;.--..
          RETLW     0xFF              ;.--.-
          RETLW     0xFF              ;.---.
          RETLW     0x31              ;1
          RETLW     0x36              ;6
          RETLW     0x3D              ;BREAK (=)
          RETLW     0x2F              ;/
          RETLW     0xFF              ;-..--
          RETLW     0xFF              ;-..-.
          RETLW     0x7E              ;CALL (->)
          RETLW     0x3C              ;(<)
          RETLW     0xFF              ;-.---
          RETLW     0x37              ;7
          RETLW     0xFF              ;--..-
          RETLW     0xFF              ;--.-.
```

201 THE FULL LISTINGS

```
            RETLW       0xFF            ;--.--
            RETLW       0x38            ;8
            RETLW       0xFF            ;---.-
            RETLW       0x39            ;9
            RETLW       0x30            ;0

XTABLE6     MOVF        MORSE, W
            ANDLW       0x3F
            ADDWF       PCL, F
            RETLW       0xFF            ;......
            RETLW       0xFF            ;.....-
            RETLW       0xFF            ;....-.
            RETLW       0xFF            ;....--
            RETLW       0xFF            ;...-..
            RETLW       0x7F            ;EOM(<-)
            RETLW       0xFF            ;...-.
            RETLW       0xFF            ;...---
            RETLW       0xFF            ;..-...
            RETLW       0xFF            ;..-..-
            RETLW       0xFF            ;..-.-.
            RETLW       0xFF            ;..-.--
            RETLW       0x3F            ;?
            RETLW       0xFF            ;..--.-
            RETLW       0xFF            ;..--..
            RETLW       0xFF            ;..----
            RETLW       0xFF            ;.-....
            RETLW       0xFF            ;.-..-.
            RETLW       0xFF            ;.-..-.
            RETLW       0xFF            ;.-.-..
            RETLW       0x2E            ;STOP
            RETLW       0xFF            ;.-.-.--
            RETLW       0xFF            ;.-.---
            RETLW       0xFF            ;.--...
            RETLW       0xFF            ;.--..-
            RETLW       0xFF            ;.--.-.
            RETLW       0xFF            ;.--.--
            RETLW       0xFF            ;.---..
            RETLW       0xFF            ;.---.-
            RETLW       0xFF            ;.----.
            RETLW       0xFF            ;.-----
            RETLW       0xFF            ;-.....
            RETLW       0xFF            ;-...-.
            RETLW       0xFF            ;-..-..
            RETLW       0xFF            ;-..-.-
            RETLW       0xFF            ;--.-.-
            RETLW       0xFF            ;-..-.-
            RETLW       0xFF            ;-..--.
            RETLW       0xFF            ;-..---
            RETLW       0xFF            ;-.-...
            RETLW       0xFF            ;-.-..-
            RETLW       0xFF            ;-.-.-.
            RETLW       0xFF            ;-.-.--
            RETLW       0xFF            ;-.-..
            RETLW       0xFF            ;-.-.-.
            RETLW       0xFF            ;-.-.--.
            RETLW       0xFF            ;-.----
            RETLW       0xFF            ;--....
            RETLW       0xFF            ;--..-.
            RETLW       0xFF            ;--..-.-
```

```
        RETLW       0x2C            ; COMMA
        RETLW       0xFF            ; --.-..
        RETLW       0xFF            ; --.-.-
        RETLW       0xFF            ; --.--.
        RETLW       0xFF            ; --.---
        RETLW       0xFF            ; ---...
        RETLW       0xFF            ; ---..-
        RETLW       0xFF            ; ---.-.
        RETLW       0xFF            ; ---.--
        RETLW       0xFF            ; ----..
        RETLW       0xFF            ; ----.-
        RETLW       0xFF            ; -----.
        RETLW       0xFF            ; ------

        END
```